Student Solutions Manual
for
Descriptive
Inorganic Chemistry
Fifth Edition

Geoff Rayner-Canham
Sir Wilfred Grenfell College

Tina Overton
University of Hull

W.H. Freeman and Company
New York

Printed in the United States of America

ISBN-13: 978-1-4292-2434-5
ISBN-10: 1-4292-2434-7

First printing

W.H. Freeman and Company
41 Madison Avenue
New York, NY 10010
Houndmills, Basingstoke
RG21 6XS England

www.whfreeman.com

Table of Contents

Chapter 1

THE ELECTRONIC STRUCTURE OF THE ATOM: A REVIEW

Exercises

1.1 (a) Surface where the electron probability is zero.

(b) No two electrons in an atom can have exactly the same set of quantum numbers.

(c) Paramagnetic—the attraction into a magnetic field by an unpaired electron.

1.3

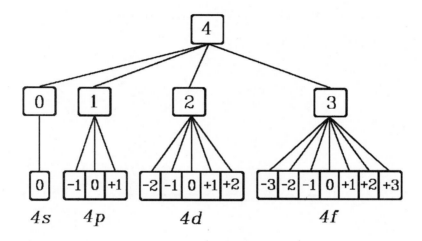

1.5 $5p$.

1.7 The quantum number n relates to the size of an orbital.

1.9 The two electrons paired and occupying the same orbital would be least favorable, because the pairing energy would be necessary to overcome the repulsive forces. Paired but in different orbitals also comes with an energy cost because there is a finite probability that the electrons will occupy the same volume of space, again resulting in a repulsive energy factor. With parallel spins there is zero probability that the electrons will occupy the same volume of space; hence this is the lowest energy condition.

1

1.11   (a) $[Ne]3s^1$; (b) $[Ar]4s^23d^8$; (c) $[Ar]4s^13d^{10}$.

1.13   (a) [Ar]; (b) [Ar]; (c) $[Ar]3d^9$.

1.15   1+ and 3+. Thallium has a noble gas core ground-state electron configuration of $[Xe]6s^24f^{14}5d^{10}6p^1$. The $6p$ electron is lost first, giving an ion of 1+ charge; the two $6s$ electrons are lost next, giving an ion of 3+ charge and corresponding to the removal of all outer electrons: $[Xe]4f^{14}5d^{10}$.

1.17   1+. Silver has a noble gas core ground state electron configuration of $[Kr]5s^14d^{10}$. The $5s$ electron is lost first, giving an ion of 1+ charge and corresponding to the removal of all outer electrons: $[Kr]4d^{10}$.

1.19   (a) 2; (b) 0; (c) 4.

$$2p \ \underline{\uparrow\downarrow} \ \underline{\uparrow} \ \underline{\uparrow} \qquad 2s \ \underline{\uparrow\downarrow}$$

(a)   (b)

$$4s \ \underline{\uparrow} \quad 3d \ \underline{\uparrow} \ \underline{\uparrow} \ \underline{\uparrow} \ \underline{\uparrow} \ \underline{\uparrow}$$

(c)

1.21   Electron configuration of atom: $[Rn]7s^25f^{14}6d^{10}7p^1$.
Electron configuration of +1 ion: $[Rn]7s^25f^{14}6d^{10}$.
Electron configuration of +3 ion: $[Rn]5f^{14}6d^{10}$.

Beyond the Basics

1.23   9, 5, 121.

1.25   There are seven f orbitals. There are (at least) two separate ways of depicting them and designating them: the general set and the cubic set. The seven solutions for the cubic set are: x^3, y^3, z^3, xyz, $z(x^2-y^2)$, $y(z^2-x^2)$, and $x(z^2-y^2)$. The f_{x3}, f_{y3}, f_{z3} resemble the d_{z2} in that they have lobes along the particular axis, but with double "doughnut" rings around the middle rather than single rings. The other f orbitals resemble the d_{x2-y2}, d_{xy}, d_{xz}, and d_{yz} orbitals in that they consist of eight lobes (rather than four) between the axes. Several texts, such as that by Huheey, discuss f orbitals. See also E.A. Ogryzlo, On the Shapes of f Orbitals, *J. Chem. Educ.* **42** (1965): 150–151 (1965) and refs. therein.

1.27   Hydrogen heads the alkali metal group even though hydrogen is a non-metal with unique properties. Helium heads the alkaline earth metal group even though helium is better classified as a noble gas.

Chapter 2

AN OVERVIEW OF THE PERIODIC TABLE

Exercises

2.1   (a) Elements scandium, yttrium, and lanthanum through lutetium.
(b) Apparent radius of an atom when it is in non-bonded contact with another atom
(c) Actual nuclear charge experienced by an electron in an atom.

2.3   There was no space for argon because it did not fit into any of the then-known groups (the noble gas group was then unknown). Also, because Mendeleev's table was based on measured atomic mass (atomic number was unknown at the time), argon (39.9) should have been placed between potassium (39.1) and calcium (40.1).

2.5   The long form of the table correctly depicts the order of elements; the disadvantage is that the table becomes very elongated.

2.7   The *-ium* ending is used normally to indicate a metal. The ending *-on* has been used for non-metals. When helium was discovered by spectroscopy to exist in the Sun, it was assumed to be a metal, and hence the wrong suffix was chosen and never subsequently changed.

2.9   With nuclei up to 26 protons, nuclear fusion is an exothermic process and is thus favored. Beyond this point, fusion is endothermic and requires the energy from a supernova explosion to happen.

2.11   (a) Lead (previously bismuth until it was realized that Bi-209 was radioactive with an extremely long half-life); (b) technetium; (c) bromine.

2.13   Sodium, because it has an odd number of protons (according to isotope tables, sodium has one stable isotope, that with 12 neutrons—an even number—while magnesium has three stable isotopes).

2.15   50. The number of neutrons must be greater than the number of protons. Fifty is the next higher "magic number" above 39, the proton number.

2.17   (a) Several nonmetals, such as iodine, and some compounds, such as FeS_2, fool's gold, have metallic lusters.
(b) Diamond, a carbon (nonmetal) allotrope, has the highest thermal conductivity of all substances.
(c) The other common carbon allotrope, graphite, also a nonmetal, is a good electrical conductor in two dimensions.

2.19   Potassium. As the effective atomic charge on the outermost electrons increases across a period, so the covalent radius will decrease, resulting in a smaller radius for calcium.

2.21   With the poorly shielding $3d$ orbitals having been filled corresponding to the added protons, the effective nuclear charge on the outer ($4p$) electrons will be increased; hence the covalent radius will decrease.

2.23   Table of effective nuclear charge for the second period elements using Slater's rules.

Element	Li	Be	B	C	N	O	F	Ne
Z	3	4	5	6	7	8	9	10
$1s$	2.65	3.65	4.65	5.65	6.65	7.65		
	8.65	9.65						
$2s$	1.30	1.95	2.60	3.25	3.90	4.55		
	5.20	5.85						
$2p$			2.60	3.25	3.90	4.55		
	5.20	5.85						

The differences between the simplistic Slater's rules and the more sophisticated Clementi and Raimondi method are quite small. The disadvantage of the Slater method is that it does not distinguish between s and p electrons in terms of shielding.

2.25   Effective nuclear charge on $4s = 2.95$; $3d = 5.60$.

2.27   Phosphorus. With increasing nuclear charge across the period, the ionization energy will increase.

2.29   Group 2. The size of the ionization energies increases rapidly between the second and third values. Hence the third and subsequent values must correspond to the ionization of inner electrons. Two outer electrons indicate that the element belongs to the alkaline earth metals (Group 2).

2.31   Electron configurations: $Na = 1s^2 2s^2 2p^6 3s^1$; $Mg = 1s^2 2s^2 2p^6 3s^2$. Because the $2s$ electrons of magnesium experience a higher effective nuclear charge than those of sodium, magnesium will have the higher first ionization energy. For sodium, the second electron to be removed will come from the inner $2p$ orbitals. Hence it will be sodium that has the higher second ionization energy. In both cases, the third electron to be removed will come from the $2p$ orbitals. The $2p$ electrons of magnesium will experience the higher effective nuclear charge. Thus magnesium will have the higher third ionization energy.

2.33   Positive. With an electron configuration of $1s^2$, any gained electron would add to the $2s$ orbital. This would experience stronger repulsions from the inner $1s$ electrons than attraction to the well-shielded nucleus. Hence it would be an endothermic process.

2.35   In each case, the preferred isotope will be that having a full shell of neutrons (126). Hence the answers are (a) 208; (b) 209; (c) 210.

Beyond the Basics

2.37   The average kinetic energy ($= \frac{1}{2}mv^2$) of all gases are the same under identical conditions of temperature. As dihydrogen and helium have such low molecular masses, their average velocities will be much higher. A sufficient number of molecules will have greater energy than the escape velocity for them to escape from the Earth's gravitational field. Over time, the vast majority of these molecules have escaped.

2.39   Element 117—let us call it X—would be a member of the halogens. It should be a solid at room temperature and exist as X_2 molecular units. It should form an anion X^-, but at the same time, X is on the border with metals, so positive oxidation states, particularly +1 and +3, should be quite common.

2.41.   No specific answer.

Chapter 3

COVALENT BONDING

Exercises

3.1   (a) The acronym for **l**inear **c**ombination of **a**tomic **o**rbitals; it is a sophisticated theory for the representation of bonding in covalent molecules.

(b) A molecular orbital in which the increased electron density lies between the two nuclei involved in the bonding.

(c) The acronym for **v**alence **s**hell **e**lectron **p**air **r**epulsion, a method of predicting molecular shape using simple electron pair concepts of bonding.

(d) Hybridization involves the concept of mixing atomic orbitals on a central atom to give hybrid orbitals that have the directions to give the maximum overlap with the atomic orbitals of the surrounding atoms.

(e) The principal axis is the axis containing the highest n-fold rotation axis.

3.3   The bond order would be $\frac{1}{2}$ and the ion would be paramagnetic.

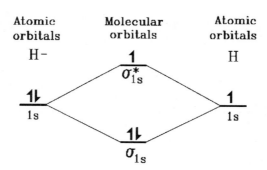

3.5   Bond order $2\frac{1}{2}$. Electron configuration: $(\sigma_{2s})^2(\sigma*_{2s})^2(\pi_{2p})^4(\sigma_{2p})^1$.

3.7   Triple bond.

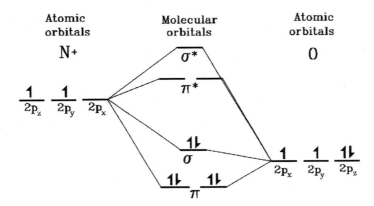

3.9   Single bond. The ordering for the earlier elements predicts two unpaired electrons, while that for the later elements predicts paired electrons. Hence if the former ordering is correct, the molecule should be paramagnetic, but the latter ordering would be diamagnetic [diboron is actually paramagnetic].

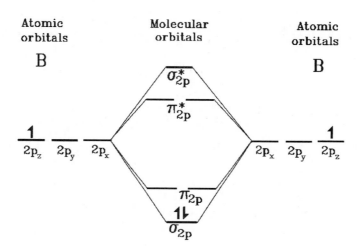

3.11   Electron dot diagrams:

(a)

(b)

(c)

(d)

3.13   (a) Electron-dot diagram; (b) resonance structures; (c) partial bond
representation. Bond order approximately $1\frac{1}{2}$.

$$\left[\;\underset{\cdot\cdot}{\overset{\cdot\cdot}{\ddot{N}}}\overset{\cdot\cdot}{\underset{\cdot\cdot}{\ddot{O}}}\right]^{-} \qquad \left[:-N\overset{O}{\underset{O}{\diagdown}}\right]^{-} \qquad \left[:-N\overset{O}{\underset{O}{\diagdown}}\right]^{-} \qquad \left[:-N\overset{O}{\underset{O}{\diagdown}}\right]^{-}$$

(a)   (b)   (c)

3.15   (a) Electron dot diagrams; (b) formal charge structures; (c) partial bond representation

$$\left[:\ddot{N}::C::\ddot{S}:\right]^{-} \quad \left[:N:::C:\ddot{S}:\right]^{-} \quad \left[:\ddot{N}:C:::S:\right]^{-}$$

(a)

**formal
charge**
$$\boxed{:\ddot{N}:\;:C:\;:\ddot{S}:} \qquad \boxed{:N:\;:C:\;:\ddot{S}:} \qquad \boxed{:\ddot{N}:\;:C:\;:S:}$$
$\ominus$ $\ominus$ $2\ominus$ $\oplus$

(b)

$$\left[N\equiv\!\!\equiv C\!\!=\!\!=\!\!=S\right]^{-}$$

(c)

3.17   (a) tetrahedral, V-shaped; (b) tetrahedral, trigonal pyramidal;
(c) trigonal bipyramidal, linear; (d) octahedral, square planar.

(a)   (b)   (c)   (d)

3.19   Linear: carbon disulfide and xenon difluoride; V-shaped: chlorine dioxide ($< 109\frac{1}{2}°$) [in fact, the bonding is not so simple, as we discuss in Chapter 16], tin(II) chloride ($< 120°$), and nitrosyl chloride ($< 120°$).

(a)   (b)   (c)

(d)   (e)

3.21   Oxygen difluoride and phosphorus trichloride. The bond angles will be reduced as a result of the presence of the lone pairs.

3.23   (a) sp^3; (b) sp^3; (c) sp^3d; (d) sp^3d^2.

3.25   The hybrid orbitals used would be sp, accounting for the linear arrangement.

2p ⎯ ⎯ ⎯	2p <u>1</u> ⎯ ⎯	2p ⎯ ⎯	2p ⎯ ⎯
		sp <u>1</u> <u>1</u>	sp <u>1↓</u> <u>1↓</u>
2s <u>1↓</u>	2s <u>1</u>		
(a)	(b)	(c)	(d)

3.27   Hydrogen selenide, because with more electrons, the dispersion forces would be greater (the slightly weaker dipole-dipole interaction than that of hydrogen sulfide is a less important factor).

3.29   Polar: oxygen difluoride and phosphorus trichloride; nonpolar: xenon difluoride and the tetrachloroiodate ion.

3.31   Ammonia, because neighboring molecules will hydrogen-bond to each other, providing a strong intermolecular force and hence a higher boiling point than phosphine, which has the weaker dipole-dipole interactions.

3.33   The possible hybridization: (a) sp; (b) sp^2; (c) sp^3; (d) sp^3d; (e) sp^3d^2.

3.35   Because methane is nonlinear, it will have (3N−6) vibrational modes. With five atoms, then it will have nine vibrational modes.

3.37   (a) There will be one C_3 axis, three C_2 axes, three σ_v planes, one σ_h plane, one improper S_6 axis, and three S_2 axes. The molecule would have D_{3h} symmetry.
        (b) There will be one C_4 axis and two σ_v planes. The molecule will have C_{4v} symmetry.

(c) There will be one C_4 axis, four C_2 axes, one σ_h plane, four σ_v planes, a center of symmetry, one improper S_4 axis, and four S_2 axes.

3.39   (a) Trigonal pyramidal. One C_3 axis and three σ_v planes. The point group will be C_{3v}.

(b) Trigonal planar. One C_3 axis, three C_2 axes, one σ_h plane, and three σ_v planes. The point group will be D_{3h}.

(c) Tetrahedral. Four C_3 axes, three C_2 axes, and six σ_v planes. The point group will be T_d.

d) Octahedral. Three C_4 axes, four C_3 axes, six C_2 axes, nine σ_v planes, and a center of symmetry.

Beyond the Basics

3.41   The following figures show the overlap of an s orbital with a typical d orbital to form a σ bond; overlap of a p orbital with a typical d orbital to form a σ bond; and overlap of a p orbital with a typical d orbital to form a π bond. Black dots indicate the location of the nuclei.

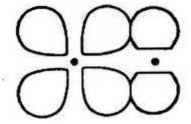

3.43   Using formal charge structures, we see that the NNO arrangement
provides two possibilities with only one formal charge per atom. **The two**
feasible formal charge structures for NON both have double cha**rges.**

3.45   The two feasible formal charge electron arrangements for the CON⁻ ion
have five formal charges! This is a very unlikely structure.

3.47 Let us look at the bond order of the product molecules in each case. NO$^+$ and CN$^-$ are both triply bonded while NO$^-$ and CN$^+$ will be double bonded. The former combination will therefore be energetically preferred.

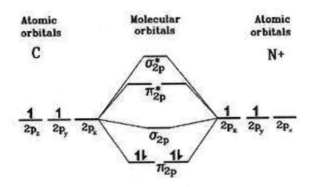

3.49   One would expect the halide with the larger number of halogen atoms to have the higher boiling point as a result of the greater number of electrons and hence the stronger dispersion forces. A possible answer (but not necessarily the correct one!) would be that antimony has an electronegativity comparable to some metals. As a result, there may be a significant ionic character to the bonding in $SbCl_3$ (the lower oxidation state and hence lower charge density species) resulting in a higher boiling point than otherwise expected.

3.51   One C_5 axis, five C_2 axes, one σ_h plane, and five σ_v planes.

3.53   To have an infrared active absorption, a bond vibration must involve a change in dipole moment. For diatomic dioxygen, there can be no vibration that results in a change of dipole moment. For triatomic molecules, such as trioxygen, an assymetrical stretch involves a change in dipole moment. Thus ozone will be infrared absorbing.

3.55   With the low planetary mass, the atmospheric gases on Mars would be lost comparatively quickly. Volcanoes provided a replenishment of the carbon dioxide into the atmosphere. Carbon dioxide is a strong radiation trapper. When the core solidified, volcanic activity ceased and no more of the 'greenhouse gas' was being pumped into the atmosphere to replace that lost due to the low gravitational field of the planet. Hence the remaining atmosphere cooled.

Chapter 4

METALLIC BONDING

Exercises

4.1 (a) A model in which it is assumed that the metal consists of metal ions with free electrons.

(b) The smallest fragment of a crystal lattice that, if repeated, will re-create the entire structure.

(c) The combination of two or more solid metals.

4.3 High electrical conductivity, high thermal conductivity, high reflectivity, and high boiling point (any three).

4.5 The overlap of the $3s$ and $3p$ bands means that electrons in the full $3s$ band can "spill over" into the $3p$ band, enabling electron mobility through the crystal lattice.

4.7 For metallic behavior, the orbitals of the atoms must overlap. In the gas phase, metal atoms are moving freely as single atoms or as discrete molecules, such as dilithium, Li_2.

4.9 Cubic and hexagonal, hexagonal being the closer packed.

4.11   The simple cubic unit cell contains $4 \times \frac{1}{4}$ atoms; that is, one atom.

4.13   The atoms must be about the same size, they must adopt the same structure, and they must have similar chemical properties.

Beyond the Basics

4.15   If we take the radius of an atom as r, then the side length of a unit cell for the simple cubic lattice will be $2r$. The volume of the atom will be $\frac{4}{3}\pi r^3$, while the volume of the cube will be $(2r)^3$. The ratio of these gives 0.52. Thus the empty space, expressed as a percentage, will be 48 percent.

4.17   The face diagonal length will be $4r$. Using Pythagoras's theorem, the length of the unit cell edge will be $[4/(2)^{\frac{1}{2}}]r = 2.83r$.

4.19   (a) Using the answer to 4.18, the metallic radius of chromium will be $288/2.31$ pm $= 125$ pm.

(b) The density can be calculated from $\dfrac{\text{unit cell mass}}{\text{unit cell volume}}$.

The unit cell volume will be $(288 \times 10^{-10}$ cm$)^3 = 2.39 \times 10^{-23}$ cm^3

Each unit cell contains two atoms, thus mass $= \dfrac{2 \times 52.0 \text{ g} \cdot \text{mol}^{-1}}{6.02 \times 10^{23} \text{ mol}^{-1}}$

$= 1.73 \times 10^{-22}$ g.

Density $= \dfrac{1.73 \times 10^{-22} \, g}{2.39 \times 10^{-23} \, cm^3} = 7.24$ g·cm^{-3}.

4.21   A face-centered cubic unit cell contains four atoms.

Thus mass $= \dfrac{4 \times 107.9 \text{ g} \cdot \text{mol}^{-1}}{6.02 \times 10^{23} \text{ mol}^{-1}} = 7.17 \times 10^{-22}$ g

Volume $= \dfrac{7.17 \times 10^{-22} \text{ g}}{10.50 \text{ g} \cdot \text{cm}^{-3}} = 6.83 \times 10^{-23}$ cm^3 $= 6.83 \times 10^7$ pm^3

Length of side $= \sqrt[3]{(6.83 \times 10^7 \text{ pm}^3)} = 409$ pm

Using the result from 4.17, radius of silver atom = (409 pm)/(2.83)

= 145 pm.

4.23   Among the most unusual properties, a suspension of gold nanoparticles has a red color.

Chapter 5

IONIC BONDING

Exercises

5.1 (a) The distortion of an anion from a spherical shape.

(b) The holes between anions in the crystal packing in which cations can fit.

(c) The diagram used to show that many elements and compounds possess combinations of the three bonding categories: metallic, covalent, and ionic.

5.3 Hard and brittle crystals; high melting points; electrically conducting in liquid phase and in aqueous solution.

5.5 (a) K^+, because the radius will be determined by the inner orbitals ($2s$ and $2p$) while the radius of K is determined by the $3s$ orbital.

(b) Ca^{2+}, because the ions are isoelectronic but calcium has one more proton, and hence a higher Z_{eff} and a smaller ionic radius.

(c) Rb^+, because again the ions are isoelectronic, with rubidium having two more protons than bromide, and hence a higher Z_{eff} and a smaller ionic radius.

5.7 NaCl, because chloride is smaller than iodide; the charge is more concentrated (charge density is higher) and the ionic attraction will be stronger in NaCl than in NaI. The stronger the ionic attraction, the higher the temperature needed to melt the ionic lattice.

5.9 Ag^+, because it has the lowest charge density.

5.11 UCl_3 (837°C); UCl_4 (590°C); UCl_5 (327°C); UCl_6 (179°). The melting points steadily decrease with increasing charge density of the uranium, resulting in increasing contribution of covalency to the bonding. In this particular series, there does not appear to be a clear divide between high (ionic) and low (covalent) melting points. The fact that uranium(V) chloride decomposes in water and is soluble in carbon disulfide would indicate that bonding in that compound is predominantly covalent.

5.13 WF_6 (2°C) and WO_3 (1472°C). The bonding in the fluoride is obviously predominantly covalent while the oxide is clearly ionic. The fluoride is more polarizable than the oxide.

5.15   Tin(II) chloride has a higher melting point because tin(II) has a fairly low charge density. The bonding in $SnCl_2$ will be predominantly ionic. The high charge density of the tin(IV) ion would result in covalent bonding for $SnCl_4$ and therefore a low melting point.

5.17   No, ionic compounds do not dissolve in nonpolar solvents, because the dissolving process requires the formation of ion-dipole interactions. Molecules of a nonpolar solvent do not possess dipoles.

5.19   Magnesium chloride, because the dipositive smaller magnesium ion has a significantly higher charge density than the monopositive larger sodium ion. The magnesium ion would therefore be likely to have a "shell" of strongly attracted water molecules to diffuse the charge.

5.21   Lithium nitrate, because the lithium ion has a higher charge density than the sodium ion. The lithium ion would therefore be more likely to have a "shell" of water molecules to diffuse the charge.

5.23   The coordination number depends on the radius ratio.

5.25   The magnesium ion is smaller than the calcium ion. Thus, presumably, only six fluoride anions can fit around a magnesium ion, compared to eight around each calcium ion.

5.27

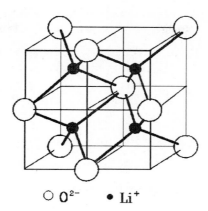

○ O²⁻   ● Li⁺

5.29   (a) Metallic and a lesser contribution of ionic; (b) covalent and a lesser contribution of ionic.

5.31   The choice would be metallic or covalent. With such a low melting point (and without seeing the element), the first choice would be covalent. A measurement of its high electrical conductivity (and observation of the metallic luster) would confirm it to have metallic bonding.

Beyond the Basics

5.33   In the solid, there is shared ionic bonding with the six nearest neighbors of each ion. In the gas phase, there is direct hybrid ionic-covalent bonding between pairs of ions.

5.35   (a) Copper(II) chloride. The higher charge density copper(II) ion will result in a higher lattice energy in its chloride and therefore a higher melting point.
(b) Lead(II) chloride. The very high charge density of the lead(IV) ion will result in the compound having essentially covalent bonding and therefore a low melting point. Ionic lead(II) chloride will have a high melting point.

5.37   The diagonal length through the center of the unit cell will be $2(r_+ + r_-)$. Using Pythagoras's theorem, the length of the unit cell edge will be $[2/(3)^{1/2}](r_+ + r_-) = 1.15(r_+ + r_-)$.

5.39   The unit cell of rubidium chloride contains four pairs of ions.

$$\text{Thus mass} = \frac{4 \times 121.0 \text{ g} \cdot \text{mol}^{-1}}{6.02 \times 10^{23} \text{ mol}^{-1}} = 8.04 \times 10^{-22} \text{ g}$$

$$\text{Volume} = \frac{8.04 \times 10^{-22} \text{ g}}{2.76 \text{ g} \cdot \text{cm}^{-3}} = 2.91 \times 10^{-22} \text{ cm}^3 = 2.91 \times 10^8 \text{ pm}^3$$

Length of side = $\sqrt[3]{(2.91 \times 10^8 \text{ pm}^3)}$ = 663 pm

Sum of ionic radii = (663 pm)/2 = 331 pm

Thus $r(\text{Rb}^+)$ = 331 pm − 167 pm = 164 pm

5.41   The unit cell of sodium hexafluoroantimonate(V) contains four pairs of ions.

$$\text{Thus mass} = \frac{4 \times 258.8 \text{ g} \cdot \text{mol}^{-1}}{6.02 \times 10^{23} \text{ mol}^{-1}} = 1.72 \times 10^{-21} \text{ g}$$

$$\text{Volume} = \frac{1.72 \times 10^{-21} \text{ g}}{4.37 \text{ g} \cdot \text{cm}^{-3}} = 3.94 \times 10^{-22} \text{ cm}^3 = 3.94 \times 10^8 \text{ pm}^3$$

Length of side = $\sqrt[3]{(3.94 \times 10^8 \text{ pm}^3)}$ = 733 pm

Sum of ionic radii = (733 pm)/2 = 367 pm

Thus $r(\text{SbF}_6^-)$ = 367 pm − 116 pm = 251 pm

5.43   Radius ratios are 0.32 (LiAt); 0.516 (NaAt); 0.676 (KAt); 0.738 (RbAt); and 0.804 (CsAt). Thus LiAt should adopt wurtzite or sphalerite packing; NaAt and KAt, sodium chloride packing; and RbAt and CsAt, cesium chloride packing.

Chapter 6

INORGANIC THERMODYNAMICS

Exercises

6.1   (a) A reaction that occurs without external "help," or a reaction for which $\Delta G°$ is negative.

(b) A measure of disorder.

(c) The enthalpy change when a mole of a substance is formed from its constituent elements in their standard phases at 298 K and 100 kPa.

6.3   The entropy change is probably negative, because according to the chemical equation, there is a decrease of one half mole of gas (gases have a much higher entropy than liquids and solids).

$$Ca(s) + \tfrac{1}{2} O_2(g) \rightarrow CaO(s)$$

If the entropy change is negative, then for a spontaneous reaction, the enthalpy change must be negative.

6.5 $\Delta H_f° = -286 \text{ kJ·mol}^{-1};$

$\Delta S_f°\ \ = [1 \times (70) - 1 \times (131) - \tfrac{1}{2} \times (205)] \text{ J·mol}^{-1}\text{·K}^{-1}$

$\qquad\quad = -163 \text{ J·mol}^{-1}\text{·K}^{-1} = -0.163 \text{ kJ·mol}^{-1}\text{·K}^{-1}$

$\Delta G_f°\ \ = -286 \text{ kJ·mol}^{-1} - (298\text{K})(-0.163 \text{ kJ·mol}^{-1}\text{·K}^{-1})$

$\qquad\quad = -237 \text{ kJ·mol}^{-1}$

The reaction is spontaneous at SATP.

6.7 $PCl_5(g) + SO_3(g) \rightarrow SO_2Cl_2(g) + POCl_3(l)$

$\Delta G° = \Sigma\Delta G_f°(\text{products}) - \Sigma\Delta G_f°(\text{reactants})$

$\Delta G° = [1 \times (-314) + 1 \times (-521)] - [1 \times (-305) + 1 \times (-371)] \text{ kJ·mol}^{-1}$

$\qquad\ = -159 \text{ kJ.mol}^{-1}$

This is only an approximate value of $\Delta G°$ because the $\Delta G_f°$ values are not those of the common phases at SATP.

6.9   The N=N bond will be stronger, because multiple bonds are stronger than single bonds between the same elements.

6.11   Bonds broken = 4(S–S) + 8(H–S) = [(4 × 266) + (8 × 363)] kJ·mol^{-1}
= 3968 kJ·mol^{-1}
Bonds formed = 8(S–S) + 4(H–H) = [(8 × 266) + (4 × 432)] kJ·mol^{-1}
= 3856 kJ·mol^{-1}
Approximate enthalpy of reaction = [3968 − 3856] kJ·mol^{-1} = +112
kJ·mol^{-1}

6.13   Sodium chloride, lithium fluoride, magnesium oxide. LiF will be higher
than NaCl because LiF has smaller, higher charge density ions. MgO will
be the highest because the charges (and thus charge densities) are higher.

6.15   The first two terms will be [8/(3)$^{1/2}$ − 6/2] = 1.62. Again, more terms must
be considered to approach the limiting value of 1.763.

6.17 $$U = -\frac{(6.02 \times 10^{23} \text{ mol}^{-1}) \times 2.519 \times 2 \times 1 \times (1.602 \times 10^{-19} \text{ C})^2}{4 \times 3.142 \times (8.854 \times 10^{-12} \text{ C}^2 \cdot \text{J}^{-1} \cdot \text{m}^{-1})(2.31 \times 10^{-10} \text{ m})}\left(1 - \frac{1}{8}\right)$$
$$= -2649 \text{ kJ·mol}^{-1}$$

6.19

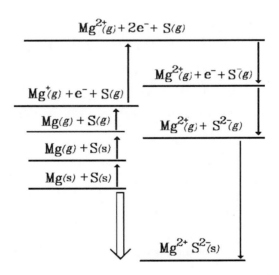

6.21   Na(s) sublimation = +107 kJ·mol^{-1}

$\frac{1}{2}$ H$_2$ bond energy = +216 kJ·mol^{-1}

Na(g) first ionization energy = +502 kJ·mol^{-1}

H(g) electron affinity (EA H) = to find

Na$^+$H$^-$ lattice energy = −782 kJ·mol^{-1}

ΔH_f°(NaCl(s)) = −411 kJ·mol^{-1}

−411 kJ·mol^{-1} = [+107 + 216 + 502 + (EA H) − 782] kJ·mol^{-1}

(EA H) = −454 kJ·mol^{-1}

6.23   Because of the high charge density of the oxide, O^{2-}, ion, the lattice energy of oxides will be very high. This will more than compensate for the net electron affinity being positive. It is the importance of the lattice energy factor that results in oxides only being stable in the solid phase.

Beyond the Basics

6.25   The term "the permittivity of free space" is a constant that relates the attractive force between two point charges. The mathematical formula is known as Coulomb's law and it has the formula

$$F = \frac{1}{4\pi\varepsilon_0}\frac{q_1 q_2}{r^2}$$

where F is the force, q_1 and q_2 are the magnitudes of the point charges, r is the distance between the charges, and ε_0 is the permittivity of free space. The permittivity of free space is an important constant throughout equations related to electric charge and electromagnetic waves. The most important relationship, perhaps, is

$$c^2 = \frac{1}{\varepsilon_0 \mu_0}$$

where c is the velocity of light and μ_0 is the permeability of free space. Thus the velocity of light is related to these two other physical constants.

6.27   As can be seen, the enthalpy of formation for both $NaCl_2$ and $NaCl_3$ are positive. Even though the lattice energies resulting from the more highly charged ions are much greater, they are not enough to compensate for the ionization of one or two $2p$ (inner) electrons.

6.29   Magnesium oxide, being a 2+/2– ion combination, will have a higher lattice energy than the 2+/1– ion combination of magnesium chloride. This energy input must be greater than the energy released from the hydration of the ions.

6.31   From the energy diagram, $\Delta H_f^\circ = -913$ kJ·mol^{-1}, while the tabulated value is -933 kJ·mol^{-1}.

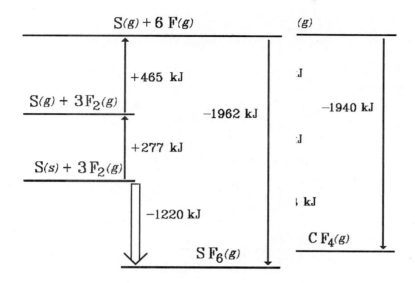

6.33   From the following energy diagram (using the ΔH_f° value from Appendix 2), the Cl–F bond energy is calculated to be 250 kJ·mol^{-1}.

6.35   The lattice energy of the calcium chloride will also be much greater. This will negate the higher hydration energy.

6.37   For calcium sulfate:

-17.8 kJ·mol^{-1} = 2653 kJ·mol^{-1} − (1650 + $\Delta H_{hydr}(SO_4^{2-})$) kJ·mol^{-1}

$\Delta H_{hydr}(SO_4^{2-})$ = -1021 kJ·mol^{-1}

For strontium sulfate:

-8.7 kJ·mol^{-1} = 2603 kJ·mol^{-1} − (1480 + $\Delta H_{hydr}(SO_4^{2-})$) kJ·mol^{-1}

$\Delta H_{hydr}(SO_4^{2-})$ = -1132 kJ·mol^{-1}

For barium sulfate:

$+19.4$ kJ·mol^{-1} = 2423 kJ·mol^{-1} − (1360 + $\Delta H_{hydr}(SO_4^{2-})$) kJ·mol^{-1}

$\Delta H_{hydr}(SO_4^{2-})$ = -1044 kJ·mol^{-1}

The values are consistent, within the errors of the data.

6.39   The cycle is shown in the diagram.

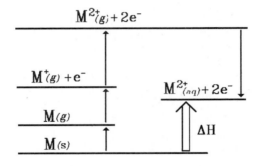

Using the values for magnesium:

ΔH = [+147 + 744 + 1457 − 1920] kJ·mol^{-1} = +428 kJ·mol^{-1}

Using the values for lead:

ΔH = [+196 + 722 + 1457 − 1477] kJ·mol^{-1} = +898 kJ·mol^{-1}

The only significant difference between the two ions is their hydration enthalpies. If we look at the charge densities, we see that the charge density for the magnesium ion is much greater than that of the lead(II) ion. Hence there will be a stronger attraction (more exothermic reaction) between the magnesium ion and the oxygen ends of water molecules than for the equivalent process with the lead(II) ion (you can also argue using comparative ionic radii because the charges are the same).

6.41 Using the Kapustinskii equation:

$$U = -\frac{1.202 \times 10^5 \times 2 \times 1 \times 1}{348}\left(1 - \frac{34.5}{348}\right) = -622 \text{ kJ·mol}^{-1}$$

compared with -668 kJ·mol^{-1} experimentally and -636 kJ·mol^{-1} from the Born-Landé equation.

6.43 According to the Appendix, the NaCl-structure lattice energy of rubidium chloride is 693 kJ·mol^{-1}. We can calculate the theoretical CsCl lattice energy using the Born-Landé equation:

$$U = -\frac{(6.02 \times 10^{23} \text{ mol}^{-1}) \times 1.763 \times 1 \times 1 \times (1.602 \times 10^{-19} \text{ C})^2}{4 \times 3.142 \times (8.854 \times 10^{-12} \text{ C}^2 \cdot \text{J}^{-1} \cdot \text{m}^{-1})(3.33 \times 10^{-10} \text{ m})}\left(1 - \frac{1}{9.5}\right)$$

$$= -657 \text{ kJ·mol}^{-1}$$

Thus the approximate ΔH for the transformation $= [(-657) - (-693)]$

$$\text{kJ·mol}^{-1}$$

$$= +36 \text{ kJ·mol}^{-1}$$

6.45 First, we have to calculate the lattice energy of NH$_4$F:

$$U = -\frac{(6.02 \times 10^{23} \text{ mol}^{-1}) \times 1.641 \times 1 \times 1 \times (1.602 \times 10^{-19} \text{ C})^2}{4 \times 3.142 \times (8.854 \times 10^{-12} \text{ C}^2 \cdot \text{J}^{-1} \cdot \text{m}^{-1})(2.56 \times 10^{-10} \text{ m})}\left(1 - \frac{1}{8}\right)$$

$$= -778 \text{ kJ·mol}^{-1}$$

Then we can construct a Born-Haber type cycle:

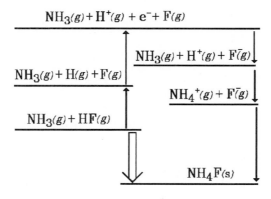

ΔH reaction can be calculated from the difference in the enthalpies of formation:

$\Delta H = [(-464) - (-273) - (-46)] \ kJ \cdot mol^{-1} = -145 \ kJ \cdot mol^{-1}$

The ionization energy of hydrogen ($+1537 \ kJ \cdot mol^{-1}$) is provided in the question.

The other information needed to complete the cycle, except for

$NH_3(g) + H^+(g) + F^-(g) \rightarrow NH_4^+(g) + F^-(g)$

is found in the appendices:

Bond energy (H–F) = $+565 \ kJ \cdot mol^{-1}$

Electron affinity F = $-328 \ kJ \cdot mol^{-1}$

$-145 \ kJ \cdot mol^{-1} =$

$[(+565) + (+1537) + (-328) + (\text{proton affinity}) + (-778)] \ kJ \cdot mol^{-1}$

proton affinity = $-1141 \ kJ \cdot mol^{-1}$

6.47   Metals certainly do not "want to lose electrons," as is apparent from the high positive values of the ionization energies. It is generally but not always true that the electron affinities for nonmetals are negative, for example; the second electron affinity of oxygen is positive. Thus ionic bond formation is best considered as a competition for electrons.

Chapter 7

ACIDS AND BASES

Exercises

7.1 Polar protic: solvents with a dielectric constant usually between 50 and 100.

Dipolar aprotic: solvents with dielectric constant usually between 20 and 50.

Nonpolar: solvents with dielectric constant close to zero.

7.3 (a) $H^+(aq) + OH^-(aq) \rightarrow H_2O(l)$

(b) $2\,HCO_3^-(aq) + Co^{2+}(aq) \rightarrow CoCO_3(s) + H_2O(l) + CO_2(g)$

(c) $OH^-(aq) + CH_3COOH(aq) \rightarrow CH_3COO^-(aq) + H_2O(l)$

7.5 (a) Pairs of species that differ in formula by one ionizable hydrogen.

(b) Solvent that undergoes its own acid-base reaction, for example,

$$HA + HA \rightleftharpoons H_2A^+ + A^-$$

(c) Ability of a substance to act as an acid or a base; for example, water can act as a base to form the hydronium ion or as an acid to form the hydroxide ion.

7.7 (a) $NH_4^+(aq) + H_2O(l) \rightleftharpoons NH_3(aq) + H_3O^+(aq)$
(no reaction for the $NO_3^-(aq)$ ion)

(b) $CN^-(aq) + H_2O(l) \rightleftharpoons HCN(aq) + OH^-(aq)$
(no reaction for the $K^+(aq)$ ion)

(c) $HSO_4^-(aq) + H_2O(l) \rightleftharpoons SO_4^{2-}(aq) + H_3O^+(aq)$
(no reaction for the $Na^+(aq)$ ion)

7.9 $ClNH_2(aq) + H_2O(l) \rightleftharpoons ClNH_3^+(aq) + OH^-(aq)$

7.11 $H_2SO_4(l) + H_2SO_4(l) \rightleftharpoons H_3SO_4^+(H_2SO_4) + HSO_4^-(H_2SO_4)$

7.13 (a) The ammonium ion, NH_4^+; (b) the amide ion, NH_2^-.

7.15 $HF(H_2SO_4) + H_2SO_4(l) \rightleftharpoons H_2F^+(H_2SO_4) + HSO_4^-(H_2SO_4)$

HF is acting as a base and H_2F^+ is the conjugate acid,

H_2SO_4 is acting as an acid and HSO_4^- is the conjugate base.

7.17 $HSeO_4^-$ (base), H_2SO_4 (conjugate acid); H_2O (acid), OH^- (conjugate base).

7.19   Because the ionization process depends on the breaking of the bond to hydrogen,

$$H_2X(aq) + H_2O(l) \rightleftharpoons H_3O^+(aq) + HX^-(aq)$$

The weaker the H–X bond, the stronger the acid. Bond energies usually decrease down a group (see Bond Energy section in Chapter 6); hence the H–Se bond will be weaker than the H–S bond. Thus hydrogen selenide will be the stronger acid.

7.21   The hydrated ion will lose one hydrogen ion in a similar manner to the hydrated iron(III) and aluminum ions:

$$[Zn(OH_2)_6]^{2+}(aq) + H_2O(l) \rightleftharpoons [Zn(OH_2)_5(OH)]^+(aq) + H_3O^+(aq)$$

7.23   Because stepwise acid-base equilibria proceed to a lesser and lesser extent, the diprotic acid must be present in the least proportion.

$$H_2NNH_2(aq) + H_2O(l) \rightleftharpoons H_2NNH_3^+(aq) + OH^-(aq)$$
$$H_2NNH_3^+(aq) + H_2O(l) \rightleftharpoons {^+H_3}NNH_3^+(aq) + OH^-(aq)$$

7.25   (a) Acidic, because aluminum is a small high-charge cation that will lose an ionizable hydrogen from one of the surrounding water molecules:

$$[Al(OH_2)_6]^{3+}(aq) + H_2O(l) \rightleftharpoons [Al(OH_2)_5(OH)]^{2+}(aq) + H_3O^+(aq)$$

(b) Neutral, because the sodium ion will stay unchanged, and the iodide ion is the conjugate base of a strong acid, so it, too, will remain unchanged.

7.27   With a smaller pK_b, A^- must be the stronger base. Hence HA must be the weaker acid. Thus HB will be the stronger acid.

7.29 $H_3PO_4(aq) + HPO_4^{2-}(aq) \rightleftharpoons 2\ H_2PO_4^-(aq)$

7.31   (a) N_2O_5; (b) CrO_3; (c) I_2O_7.

7.33   (a) SiO_2 (acid), Na_2O (base); (b) NOF (acid), ClF_3 (base); (c) Al_2Cl_6 (acid), PF_3 (base).

7.35   (a) No effect.

        (b) Increasing pH (moderately large change)
$$Se^{2-}(aq) + H_2O(l) \rightleftharpoons HSe^-(aq) + OH^-(aq)$$

        (c) Decreasing pH (large change by analogy with aluminum ion)
$$[Sc(OH_2)_6]^{3+}(aq) + H_2O(l) \rightleftharpoons [Sc(OH_2)_5(OH)]^{2+}(aq) + H_3O^+(aq)$$

        (d) Increasing pH (small change)
$$F^-(aq) + H_2O(l) \rightleftharpoons HF(aq) + OH^-(aq)$$

7.37   (a) Weakly basic; (b) neutral; (c) moderately basic; (d) strongly basic.

7.39   (a) Strongly basic; (b) very strongly basic.

7.41   The chemical reaction is
$$MgO(s) + H_2O(l) \rightarrow Mg(OH)_2(s)$$
$\Delta G°$ $= [1(-834) - 1(-569) - 1(-237)]$ kJ·mol^{-1}
$= -28$ kJ·mol^{-1}

Compared with the series in the text, magnesium oxide will be a weaker base than calcium oxide ($\Delta G° = -59$ kJ·mol^{-1}).

7.43 NO^+ is a Lewis acid because it is an electron pair acceptor; similarly, Cl^- is a Lewis base because it is an electron pair donor (when they combine to form NOCl).
$(NO)(AlCl_4)(NOCl) + [(CH_3)_4N]Cl(NOCl) \rightarrow [(CH_3)_4N](AlCl_4)(NOCl) + NOCl(l)$

7.45 $NH_3(NH_3) + NH_3(NH_3) \rightleftharpoons NH_4^+(NH_3) + NH_2^-(NH_3)$

        (a) $K = [NH_4^+][NH_2^-] = 1 \times 10^{-33}$ since $[NH_4^+] = [NH_2^-]$
               $[NH_4^+] = 3 \times 10^{-17}$ mol·L^{-1}

        (b)   Let $[NH_4^+] = x$, then $[NH_2^-] = 1.0 + x$
               $K = (x)(1.0 + x) = 1 \times 10^{-33}$

Assume $x \ll 1.0$

$x = 1 \times 10^{-33}$ mol·L^{-1} = [NH$_4^+$]

7.47   (a) No. The reactants have the combinations borderline-borderline and hard-hard, while the products have combinations borderline-hard and hard-borderline. These like combinations are preferred over the mixed combinations that would result in the products.

(b) Yes. For the reactants, hard titanium(IV) ion is combined with soft iodide ion, soft titanium(II) ion with hard fluoride ion. The products will be preferred where hard-hard and soft-soft combinations result.

7.49   (a) Greater than unity, because silver ion is soft, as is cyanide ion, and chloride ion is hard.

(b) Less than unity, because both mercury and iodide ions are soft, and chloride ion is hard.

7.51   (a) Because thallium(I) is a large soft cation, it will probably have an insoluble chloride, TlCl, and precipitate with the other soft cations, silver(I), lead(II), and mercury(I) in analysis group I.

(b) Rubidium ion would behave like the other alkali metals in analysis group V and not give a precipitate (it would give a precipitate with a very large anion, as does potassium).

(c) Radium would probably behave like the other alkaline earth metals (analysis group IV) and give a precipitate of RaCO$_3$ with carbonate ion.

(d) Iron(III) would probably resemble chromium(III) and aluminum(III) and give a precipitate of Fe(OH)$_3$ upon addition of hydroxide ion in the analysis group III.

7.53   (a) MgSO$_4$; (b) CoS.

Beyond the Basics

7.55   We start by writing the relevant equilibria:

$$H_2S(aq) + H_2O(l) \rightleftharpoons H_3O^+(aq) + HS^-(aq) \qquad K_{a1} = 8.9 \times 10^{-8}$$

$$HS^-(aq) + H_2O(l) \rightleftharpoons H_3O^+(aq) + S^{2-}(aq) \qquad K_{a2} = 1.2 \times 10^{-13}$$

$$CdS(s) \rightleftharpoons Cd^{2+}(aq) + S^{2-}(aq) \qquad K_{sp} = 1.6 \times 10^{-28}$$

$$FeS(s) \rightleftharpoons Fe^{2+}(aq) + S^{2-}(aq) \qquad K_{sp} = 6.3 \times 10^{-18}$$

Then combine the acid ionization constants:

$$K_{a1} \times K_{a2} = \left(\frac{[H_3O^+][HS^-]}{[H_2S]}\right)\left(\frac{[H_3O^+][S^{2-}]}{[HS^-]}\right) = \left(\frac{[H_3O^+]^2[S^{2-}]}{[H_2S]}\right)$$

We can solve for sulfide ion concentration:

$$[S^{2-}] = (8.9 \times 10^{-8})(1.2 \times 10^{-13})\left(\frac{(0.010)}{(1.0)^2}\right) = 1.1 \times 10^{-22}$$

For cadmium ion: $[Cd^{2+}][S^{2-}] = (0.010)(1.1 \times 10^{-22}) = 1.1 \times 10^{-24}$.
This is greater than K_{sp}; thus cadmium sulfide will precipitate.

For iron(II) ion: $[Fe^{2+}][S^{2-}] = 1.1 \times 10^{-24}$.
This is less than K_{sp}; thus iron(II) sulfide will not precipitate.

7.57   Mercury(II) ion is a soft acid, so it will be found as ores of soft bases, such as sulfide ion. Zinc is a borderline acid, so it can be found as ores of both hard and soft bases.

7.59 $H_2CO_3(aq) + MgSiO_4(s) \rightarrow H_2O(l) + SiO_2(s) + MgCO_3(s)$
Thus, over geological time, the atmospheric concentration of carbon dioxide has decreased, in part due to the formation of magnesium (and calcium) carbonate minerals.

7.61   Dimethylsulfoxide must be a softer base than water, thus favoring the soft acid copper(I) rather than the borderline copper(II) ion.

7.63   In terms of the HSAB concept, the harder calcium ion is likely to form a stronger bond to the water molecules of hydration than the softer barium ion, thus driving the reaction towards solution.
$CaCl_2(s) \rightarrow Ca^{2+}(aq) + 2\ Cl^-(aq)$
In thermodynamic terms, the enthalpy (and free energy) of hydration of the calcium ion compared to the lattice energy of calcium chloride must be greater than the enthalpy of hydration of the barium ion compared to the lattice energy of barium chloride.

7.65   Aluminum oxide would act as an acid while iron(III) oxide would be a base, according to Lux-Flood theory. Thus the product should be $Fe^{3+}(AlO_6)^{3-}$.

Chapter 8

OXIDATION AND REDUCTION

Exercises

8.1 (a) A substance that will oxidize another, itself being reduced.

(b) A two-dimensional plot of free energy against temperature for series of reactions that involve elements and their oxides, sulfides, or chlorides, etc. An Ellingham diagram is used for the prediction of reaction feasibility.

8.3 (a) $4[N_{ox}(P)] + 6(-2) = 0$
            $[N_{ox}(P)] = +3$

(b) $3(+1) + [N_{ox}(P)] + 4(-2) = 0$
            $[N_{ox}(P)] = +5$

(c) $3(+1) + [N_{ox}(P)] = 0$
            $[N_{ox}(P)] = -3$

(d) $[N_{ox}(P)] + 4(+1) = +1$
            $[N_{ox}(P)] = -3$

(e) $[N_{ox}(P)] + 1(-2) + 3(-1) = 0$
            $[N_{ox}(P)] = +5$

8.5 (a) −2; (b) +2; (c) −1; (d) +6; (e) −2.

The diagrams show how the answers for (a), (b), (c), and (e) were derived.

H ∶ S̈ ∶ H	∶C̈l∶S̈∶C̈l∶	H ∶ S̈⌐S̈ ∶ H	Ö ∷ C ∷ S̈
+1 −2 +1	−1 +2 −1	+1 −1 −1 +1	−2 +4 −2
(a)	(b)	(c)	(e)

8.7 −1, +1, +3, +5, +7.

8.9 (a) +1; (b) +2; (c) +3; (d) +4; (e) +5. An increase by units of +1 from Group 13 to Group 17.

8.11 (a) Nickel from +2 to 0, carbon from 0 to +2.

(b) Manganese from +7 to +2, sulfur from +4 to +6.

8.13 $NH_4^+(aq) + 3 H_2O(l) \rightarrow NO_3^-(aq) + 10 H^+(aq) + 8 e^-$

8.15 $N_2H_4(aq) + 4 OH^-(aq) \rightarrow N_2(g) + 4 H_2O(l) + 4 e^-$

8.17   (a) $5 HBr(aq) + HBrO_3(aq) \rightarrow 3 Br_2(aq) + 3 H_2O(l)$

      (b) $2 HNO_3(aq) + Cu(s) + 2 H^+(aq) \rightarrow$
$$2 NO_2(g) + Cu^{2+}(aq) + 2 H_2O(l)$$

8.19   (a) $12 V(s) + 10 ClO_3^-(aq) + 18 OH^-(aq) \rightarrow$
$$6 HV_2O_7^{3-}(aq) + 10 Cl^-(aq) + 6 H_2O(l)$$

      (b) $2 S_2O_4^{2-}(aq) + 3 O_2(g) + 4 OH^-(aq) \rightarrow$
$$4 SO_4^{2-}(aq) + 2 H_2O(l)$$

8.21   (a) $Cu^+(aq) \rightarrow Cu^{2+}(aq) + e^-$ $E° = -0.16$ V

             $Cu^+(aq) + e^- \rightarrow Cu(s)$ $E° = +0.52$ V

Net $E°$ is positive, hence spontaneous.

      (b) $Fe^{2+}(aq) \rightarrow Fe^{3+}(aq) + e^-$ $E° = -0.77$ V

             $Fe^{2+}(aq) + 2 e^- \rightarrow Fe(s)$ $E° = -0.44$ V

Net $E°$ is negative, hence nonspontaneous.

8.23   For $Cr^{3+} \rightarrow Cr^{2+}$, $E° = -0.424$ V

There are several possibilities for oxidizing agents, one being

$Zn \rightarrow Zn^{2+}$, $E° = +0.762$ V

8.25   (a) $Au^{3+}(aq) + 3 e^- \rightarrow Au(s)$ would be the stronger oxidizing agent.

      (b) $Al(s) \rightarrow Al^{3+}(aq) + 3 e^-$ would be the stronger reducing agent.

8.27 $Pb^{2+}(aq) + 2 e^- \rightarrow Pb(s)$ $E° = -0.125$ V

$$E = E° - \frac{RT}{nF} \ln\left(\frac{1}{[Pb^{2+}]}\right)$$

$$E = (-0.125 \text{ V}) - \frac{8.31 \text{ V} \cdot \text{C} \cdot \text{mol}^{-1} \cdot \text{K}^{-1} \times 298 \text{ K}}{2 \times (9.65 \times 10^4 \text{ C} \cdot \text{mol}^{-1})} \ln\left(\frac{1}{1.5 \times 10^{-5}}\right) = -0.267 \text{ V}$$

8.29   pH = 7.00, thus $[H^+] = 1.0 \times 10^{-7}$

$$E = E° - \frac{RT}{nF} \ln\left(\frac{1}{[H^+]^4(pO_2)}\right)$$

$$E = (+1.229 \text{ V}) - \frac{8.31 \text{ V}\cdot\text{C}\cdot\text{mol}^{-1}\cdot\text{K}^{-1} \times 298 \text{ K}}{4 \times (9.65 \times 10^4 \text{ C}\cdot\text{mol}^{-1})} \ln\left(\frac{1}{(1.0 \times 10^{-7})^4 \left(20 \text{ kPa}\middle/ 100 \text{ kPa}\right)}\right)$$

$$= +0.805 \text{ V}$$

8.31   (a) Br_2

(b) $BrO_3^-(aq) \rightarrow HBrO(aq)$ is a four-electron reduction (+5 to +1 oxidation state), so $\Delta G° = -4(F)(+0.54)$.

$HBrO(aq) \rightarrow \frac{1}{2} Br_2(aq)$ is a one-electron reduction, so $\Delta G° = -1(F)(+0.45)$.

Total $\Delta G° = (-2.16F) + (-0.45F) = -2.61F$

$E° = -(-2.61F)/5F = +0.52 \text{ V}$

(c) The reduction half-reaction does not contain H^+ or OH^-:

$\frac{1}{2} Br_2(aq) + e^- \rightarrow Br^-(aq)$

Hence the Nernst expression does not have a pH-dependent term.

8.33   The most thermodynamically stable oxidation state is +3. The metal is a very strong reducing agent while cerium(IV) is an oxidizing agent.

8.35   Perchorate ion is a stronger oxidizing agent at pH 0.00 because the reduction potential is +1.201 V at pH 0.00 compared to +0.374 V at pH 14.00.

Beyond the Basics

8.37 $C(s) + O_2(g) \rightarrow CO_2(g)$

$2\,C(s) + O_2(g) \rightarrow 2\,CO(g)$

The oxidation of carbon to carbon dioxide involves a near-zero entropy change; thus the slope of the ΔG versus temperature line will be close to zero. The oxidation to carbon monoxide, however, involves an increase of entropy (one mole of gas to two moles of gas); thus the $T\Delta S$ term will become increasingly negative with increase in temperature. The negative slope for this line will ultimately cross the carbon dioxide line, making the carbon monoxide production preferred at higher temperatures.

For oxidation to carbon dioxide:

$\Delta H^\circ = -394 \text{ kJ·mol}^{-1}$

$\Delta S^\circ = [(+214) - (+205) - (+6)] \text{ J·mol}^{-1}\text{·K}^{-1} = +3 \text{ J·mol}^{-1}\text{·K}^{-1}$

$\Delta G^\circ = (-394 \text{ kJ·mol}^{-1}) - T(+0.003 \text{ kJ·mol}^{-1}\text{·K}^{-1})$

For oxidation to carbon monoxide:

$\Delta H^\circ = 2(-111) \text{ kJ·mol}^{-1} = -222 \text{ kJ·mol}^{-1}$

$\Delta S^\circ = [2(+198) - (+205) - 2(+6)] \text{ J·mol}^{-1}\text{·K}^{-1} = +179 \text{ J·mol}^{-1}\text{·K}^{-1}$

$\Delta G^\circ = (-222 \text{ kJ·mol}^{-1}) - T(-0.179 \text{ kJ·mol}^{-1}\text{·K}^{-1})$

At the crossover point, the values for ΔG° will be the same, thus

$(-394 \text{ kJ·mol}^{-1}) - T(+0.003 \text{ kJ·mol}^{-1}\text{·K}^{-1}) =$

$(-222 \text{ kJ·mol}^{-1}) - T(+0.179 \text{ kJ·mol}^{-1}\text{·K}^{-1})$

$T(0.182 \text{ kJ·mol}^{-1}\text{·K}^{-1}) = +172 \text{ kJ·mol}^{-1}$

$T = 766 \text{ K} = 493^\circ\text{C}$

8.39   In the well water at about pH 7 and E° about 0, the manganese will be present as the colorless 2+ ion. On exposure to air (oxidizing conditions), E° will increase to the point where insoluble (brown) manganese(III) oxide will be formed, thus discoloring the toilet bowl.

Chapter 9

PERIODIC TRENDS

Exercises

9.1   (a) A pair of elements in a compound whose sum of valence electrons adds up to eight.

(b) The relationship between an element and the element to its lower right in the periodic table. The diagonal relationship is found in the top left-hand corner of the periodic table.

9.3   An alum has the general formula: $M^+M^{3+}(SO_4^{2-})_2 \cdot 12H_2O$ or more correctly, $M^+[M(OH_2)_6]^{3+}(SO_4^{2-})_2 \cdot 6H_2O$, where M^+ is a large monopositive ion such as potassium or ammonium and M^{3+} is a small tripositive ion such as aluminum, chromium(III), or iron(III).

9.5   KF (m.p. 858°C), CaF_2 (m.p. 1418°C), GaF_3 (m.p. >1000°C), GeF_4 (m.p. −15°C), AsF_5 (m.p. −80°C), SeF_6 (m.p. <−35°C), BrF_5 (m.p. −60°C), KrF_2 (decomposes) [information from www.webelements.com]
The bonding in the potassium and calcium fluorides is ionic, while that for the germanium, arsenic, selenium, bromine, and krypton compounds is covalent. Assuming that the trend follows that of other series, the gallium compound is probably network covalent.

(a) The melting point decreases down the group as a result of the metallic bond throughout the metal lattice being weaker as the metal atoms become larger as the group is descended.

(b) The melting point increases down the group as the dispersion (London) forces between pairs of the covalently bonded atoms become stronger due to the increasing number of electrons.

(c) Carbon, at the top of the Group 14 elements, is network covalently bonded thus has a very high melting point. So is silicon. With germanium, tin, and lead, there is weak metallic bonding and thus low melting points.

9.7   (a) Hydrogen gas, H_2; (b) calcium metal.

9.9   As the group is descended, the cation radii increase (the charge density decreases). As a result the ionic bond will weaken and the melting point will be lower.

9.11   Scandium hydroxide, $Sc(OH)_3$.

9.13 $SO_3(s) + H_2O(l) \rightarrow H_2SO_4(aq)$
        $CrO_3(s) + H_2O(l) \rightarrow H_2CrO_4(aq)$

9.15   (a) Al_2O_3, Sc_2O_3.
        (b) P_2O_5, V_2O_5 (actually the phosphorus(V) oxide is usually written as P_4O_{10} to reflect its molecular structure).

9.17   Tin.

9.19   The other elements exist as dimers, N_2, O_2, F_2; thus they have nearly twice the number of electrons as monatomic neon and hence significantly higher melting points resulting from the stronger dispersion (London) forces.

9.21   Europium has the electron configuration $[Xe]6s^2 4f^7$. Forming the Eu^{2+} ion would retain the half-filled d orbital set.

9.23   (a) Indium(III) and bismuth(III); (b) cadmium(II) and lead(II).

9.25   Thallium(I) bromide (m.p. 460°C according to *Lange's Handbook of Chemistry*).

9.27   (a) $C\equiv O$; (b) $(C\equiv C)^{2-}$.

9.29   Yttrium, as its 3+ ion will be closest in size to the lanthanoid ions. In fact, yttrium was discovered along with many of the lanthanoid elements in ores near the Swedish town of Ytterby. Hence the name of yttrium and those of ytterbium, terbium, and erbium.

Beyond the Basics

9.31   Because the synthetic route involves a negative free energy change. For example, one synthetic route is:

$$SiCl_4(l) + 4\ NaH(s) \rightarrow SiH_4(g) + 4\ NaCl(s)$$

ΔG_f° \quad -620 \qquad -33 \qquad $+57$ \qquad -384

$\Delta G^{\circ} = [1 \times (+57) + 4 \times (-384)] - [1 \times (-620) + 4 \times (-33)]$ kJ·mol^{-1}

\qquad $= -727$ kJ·mol^{-1}

Thus, although the hydrogenation of the silicon tetrachloride by itself is unfavorable, the formation of sodium chloride from sodium hydride provides the "driving force" for the reaction.

9.33   Add excess hydroxide ion (Table 9.19). Magnesium hydroxide is basic, thus there will be a white precipitate of magnesium hydroxide. Zinc hydroxide will initally give a matching white precipitate, but being amphoteric, in excess hydroxide ion, the precipitate will redissolve.

$Mg^{2+}(aq) + 2\ OH^-(aq) \rightarrow Mg(OH)_2(s)$

$Zn^{2+}(aq) + 2\ OH^-(aq) \rightarrow Zn(OH)_2(s)$

$Zn(OH)_2(s) + 2\ OH^-(aq) \rightarrow [Zn(OH)_4]^{2-}(aq)$

9.35   (a) 12$-$, (b) 7. The formula showing the theoretical oxidation states would be $(Zn^{2+})_7[(P^{5+})_{12}(N^{3-})_{24}](Cl^-)_2$, compared with $(Na^+)_8[(Al^{3+})_{12}(Si^{4+})_6(O^{2-})_{24}](Cl^-)_2$.

9.37   Li (+1); Be (+2); B (+3); C (+4); N (+3); O (+2). For Period 2, the oxidation numbers reach a maximum at carbon, then decrease as nitrogen and oxygen cannot exceed the octet in their bonding.
Na (+1); Mg (+2); Al (+3); Si (+4); P (+5); S (+6); Cl (+5). For Period 3, the oxidation number matches the number of valence electrons except for chlorine, which, as mentioned in the text, is most probably unable to attain the highest oxidation number for steric reasons.

9.39 Fe_2O_3 (+3); RuO_4 (+8); OsO_4 (+8). For ruthenium and osmium, the oxidation number is the same as the Group number.

9.41

	Group 15	Group 16	Group 17
Group 15	CN_2^{2-}	OCN^-	FCN
Group 16	OCN^-	CO_2	FCO^+

Chapter 10

HYDROGEN

Exercises

10.1 (a) A hydrogen atom bridging two (or more) other atoms in a covalent bond in which the hydrogen is less electronegative than the atoms to which it is bonded.

(b) A hydrogen atom bridging two (or more) other atoms in a covalent bond in which the hydrogen is more electronegative than the atoms to which it is bonded.

10.3 The ice cube consists of "heavy" water, deuterium oxide, which has a higher density than normal water and will therefore sink in normal water.

10.5 The difference in absorption frequency is very small, about 10^{-6} of the signal itself. Thus ppm is a convenient unit.

10.7 Unlike the halogens, hydrogen rarely forms a negative ion, nor is it highly reactive like the halogens.

10.9 Enthalpy driven. The chemical equation is
$$N_2(g) + 3\,H_2(g) \rightarrow 2\,NH_3(g)$$
There is a decrease in the number of gas molecules, and hence a decrease in entropy. Thus for the reaction to be spontaneous, the reaction has to be exothermic.

10.11 (a) $2\,KHCO_3(s) \rightarrow K_2CO_3(s) + H_2O(g) + CO_2(g)$

(b) $HC\equiv CH(g) + 2\,H_2(g) \rightarrow H_3C-CH_3(g)$

(c) $PbO_2(s) + 2\,H_2(g) \rightarrow Pb(s) + 2\,H_2O(g)$

(d) $CaH_2(s) + H_2O(l) \rightarrow Ca(OH)_2(aq) + H_2(g)$

10.13   See the diagram. The much lesser enthalpy of formation of ammonia
compared to water can be explained in terms of the much greater bond
energy of dinitrogen (945 kJ·mol^{-1}) compared with that of dioxygen (498
kJ·mol^{-1}).

10.15   There are three categories of covalent hydrides: those in which the
hydrogen is nearly neutral; those in which it is quite positive, and those in
which it is negative. Most covalent hydrides belong in the first category;
these are the low-polarity hydrides with low boiling points (except the
long-chain hydrocarbons, where the dispersion forces become very
significant). The second category consists of ammonia, water, and
hydrogen fluoride, where hydrogen bonding (a protonic bridge) raises the
melting and boiling points above those of the first category. Finally, there
are the electron-deficient compounds of boron, where hydridic bridges
form part of the molecular structure.

10.17   KH (m.p. 417°C); CaH$_2$ (m.p. 816°C), GaH$_3$ (m.p. −15°C), GeH$_4$ (m.p.
−165°C), AsH$_3$ (m.p. −116°C), H$_2$Se (m.p. −86°C), HBr (m.p. −89°C).
The trend is to increase by one H until germanium, then a stepwise
decrease by one H to hydrogen bromide. The first two members of the
series can be categorized as ionic on the basis of their (comparatively)
high melting points [while GeH$_4$ through HBr are small molecule covalent
and GaH$_3$ is polymeric in the solid, forming a dimer in the gas]. See for
similar series Chapter 9, Table 9.9.

10.19   (a) Gas. It is a covalent hydride but not one of the three elements exhibiting strong hydrogen bonding (nitrogen, oxygen, fluorine).
(b) Solid. This is an ionic hydride.

10.21   The closeness of the electronegativities of hydrogen and carbon (thus making the C–H bond of low polarity), and the ability to hydrogen bond.

Beyond the Basics

10.23   (a) Yes, liquid; (b) no, gas; (c) yes, liquid; (d) no, gas.

10.25.   Looking at a generic Born-Haber cycle, where X = H or Cl, we see that there are two features that differ, depending upon X—the bond energy and the electron affinity.

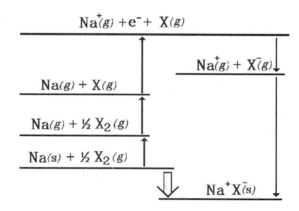

	Hydrogen	Chlorine
Bond energy	432 kJ·mol^{-1}	240 kJ·mol^{-1}
Electron affinity	−79 kJ·mol^{-1}	−349 kJ·mol^{-1}

Thus the difference results from the H–H bond being much stronger than the Cl–Cl bond, while the electron affinity of chlorine is much greater than that of hydrogen.

10.27   Hydrogen and carbon monoxide.
$$H_2O(l) + C(s) \rightarrow H_2(g) + CO(g)$$
The combustion reaction would therefore be:
$$H_2(g) + CO(g) + O_2(g) \rightarrow H_2O(g) + CO_2(g)$$
$$\Delta H = [(1 \text{ mol})(-242) + (1 \text{ mol})(-394) - (1 \text{ mol})(-111)] \text{ kJ·mol}^{-1}$$

$= -525$ kJ

Per mole, this is $-525/2$ kJ·mol^{-1} = -262 kJ·mol^{-1}, compared with -242 kJ·mol^{-1} for the combustion of pure dihydrogen. So there is about an 8 percent higher energy availability provided, and we consider the water to be produced in the gas phase (assuming the synthesis does produce the precise stoichiometric mixture).

Chapter 11

THE GROUP 1 ELEMENTS: THE ALKALI METALS

Exercises

11.1 (a) $2\,Na(s) + 2\,H_2O(l) \rightarrow 2\,NaOH(aq) + H_2(g)$

(b) $Rb(s) + O_2(g) \rightarrow RbO_2(s)$

(c) $2\,KOH(s) + CO_2(g) \rightarrow K_2CO_3(s) + H_2O(l)$

(d) $2\,NaNO_3(s) \rightarrow 2\,NaNO_2(s) + O_2(g)$

11.3 They resemble "typical" metals in that they are shiny and silvery and good conductors of heat and electricity. The alkali metals differ from "typical" metals in that they are soft, extremely chemically reactive, and have low melting points and very low densities.

11.5 Any three of the following:
All common chemical compounds are water soluble.
They always form ions of +1 oxidation state.
Their compounds are almost always ionic.
The low-charge-density alkali metal ions stabilize large low-charge anions such as hydrogen carbonate.
Their compounds are rarely hydrated.

11.7 The most likely argument is that the hydroxide ion can hydrogen bond with the surrounding water molecules whereas the chloride ion can only form ion-dipole attractions. This hydrogen bond formation would release more energy than the ion-dipole formation. Alternatively, we can simply argue that the smaller hydroxide ion will have a higher charge density and the ion-dipole attractions will be greater—this is the same argument, just a different approach. In fact, the hydration enthalpy for the hydroxide ion is indeed much greater than that of the chloride ion.

11.9 Because the equilibrium of the synthesis reaction
$$Na(l) + KCl(l) \rightarrow K(l) + NaCl(l)$$

lies to the left. To make the reaction shift right, the potassium, which boils at a lower temperature than sodium, must be continuously removed as a gas.

11.11   (a) Sodium hydroxide; (b) anhydrous sodium carbonate; (c) sodium carbonate decahydrate.

11.13   (a) Loss of water by a hydrated salt in a low-humidity environment. (b) Chemical similarities of one element and the element to its lower right in the periodic table.

11.15

$$CO_2(g) + NH_3(aq) + H_2O(l) \rightarrow NH_4^+(aq) + HCO_3^-(aq)$$
$$HCO_3^-(aq) + Na^+(aq) \rightarrow NaHCO_3(s)$$
$$2\ NaHCO_3(s) \rightarrow Na_2CO_3(s) + H_2O(g) + CO_2(g)$$
$$CaCO_3(s) \rightarrow CaO(s) + CO_2(g)$$
$$CaO(s) + H_2O(l) \rightarrow Ca(OH)_2(s)$$
$$2\ NH_4^+(aq) + 2\ Cl^-(aq) + Ca(OH)_2(s)$$
$$\rightarrow 2\ NH_3(aq) + CaCl_2(aq) + 2\ H_2O(l)$$

The problems are the disposal of waste calcium chloride and the high energy requirements of the process.

11.17   The ammonium ion is monopositive, like the alkali metals (unlike most other metals that have 2+ or higher charge); its salts are all soluble, like those of the alkali metal salts; its size is about the middle of the alkali metal ion range; all its common salts are colorless, like those of the alkali metals.

11.19   Potassium dioxide(1−) has a lower molar mass than the equivalent cesium compound. For launch, minimum mass for the same oxygen-generating capacity is crucial. Also, the common potassium salts are much lower in cost than those of cesium.

11.21   The ammonium ion is large and hence resembles the lower alkali metal
ions. In particular, its non-spherical shape makes it resemble the largest of
the alkali metal ions.

11.23   Lithium:

$$6 \, Li(s) + N_2(g) \rightarrow 2 \, Li_3N(s)$$

$$2 \, Li(s) + Cl_2(g) \rightarrow 2 \, LiCl(s)$$

$$Li(s) + C_4H_9Cl(solv) \rightarrow LiC_4H_9(solv) + LiCl(s)$$

$$4 \, Li(s) + O_2(g) \rightarrow 2 \, Li_2O(s)$$

$$2 \, Li(s) + H_2O(l) \rightarrow 2 \, LiOH(aq) + H_2(g)$$

$$Li_2O(s) + H_2O(l) \rightarrow 2 \, LiOH(aq)$$

$$2 \, LiOH(aq) + CO_2(g) \rightarrow Li_2CO_3(aq) + H_2O(l)$$

$$Li_2O(s) + CO_2(g) \rightarrow Li_2CO_3(s)$$

Sodium:

$$2 \, Na(s) + Cl_2(g) \rightarrow 2 \, NaCl(s)$$

$$2 \, Na(s) + H_2O(l) \rightarrow 2 \, NaOH(aq) + H_2(g)$$

$$2 \, Na(s) + O_2(g) \rightarrow Na_2O_2(s)$$

$$Na_2O_2(g) + H_2O(l) \rightarrow 2 \, NaOH(aq) + H_2O_2(aq)$$

$$2 \, NaOH(aq) + CO_2(g) \rightarrow Na_2CO_3(aq) + H_2O(l)$$

$$Na_2CO_3(aq) + CO_2(g) + H_2O(l) \rightarrow 2 \, NaHCO_3(aq)$$

$$2 \, Na(s) + 2 \, NH_3(l) \rightarrow 2 \, NaNH_2(NH_3) + H_2(g)$$

$$Na_2O_2(s) + CO_2(g) \rightarrow Na_2CO_3(s) + O_2(g)$$

Potassium

$$Na(l) + KCl(l) \rightarrow K(g) + NaCl(l)$$

$$2 \, K(s) + Cl_2(g) \rightarrow 2 \, KCl(s)$$

$$K(s) + O_2(g) \rightarrow KO_2(s)$$

$$2 \, KO_2(s) + 2 \, H_2O(l) \rightarrow 2 \, KOH(aq) + H_2O_2(aq) + O_2(g)$$

$$2 \, K(s) + 2 \, H_2O(l) \rightarrow 2 \, KOH(aq) + H_2(g)$$

$$2 \, KOH(aq) + CO_2(g) \rightarrow K_2CO_3(aq) + H_2O(l)$$

$$K_2CO_3(aq) + CO_2(g) + H_2O(l) \rightarrow 2 \, KHCO_3(aq)$$

$$2 \, KO_2(s) + CO_2(g) \rightarrow K_2CO_3(s) + 2 \, O_2(g)$$

$$3 \, K^+(aq) + [Co(NO_2)_6]^{3-}(aq) \rightarrow K_3[Co(NO_2)_6](s)$$

Beyond the Basics

11.25   Mass of sodium $= 1.00 \text{ t} \times (10^6 \text{ g})/(1 \text{ t}) = 1.00 \times 10^6 \text{ g}$

Mole sodium $= (1.00 \times 10^6 \text{ g}) \times (1 \text{ mol})/(23.0 \text{ g}) = 4.35 \times 10^4 \text{ mol}$

$Na^+(NaCl) + e^- \rightarrow Na(l)$

Thus mole electrons $= 4.35 \times 10^4 \text{ mol}$

$$\text{Current} = (4.35 \times 10^4 \text{ mol}) \times \frac{(9.65 \times 10^4 \text{ A} \cdot \text{V} \cdot \text{s})}{(1 \text{ mol})(7.0 \text{ V})(86400 \text{ s})} = 6.94 \times 10^4 \text{ A}$$

11.27   In the series LiF to CsF, there is an increasing mismatch in ion sizes; thus the lattice energy will decrease more than otherwise expected. As a result, the enthalpies of formation will decrease. For the series LiI to CsI, there is a decreasing mismatch in ion sizes; thus the lattice energy will decrease to a lesser extent than otherwise expected. As a result the enthalpies of formation will increase.

11.29   Sodium fluoride will be the less soluble because there is a close match in ion sizes resulting in a higher lattice energy ($Na^+ = 116$ pm; $F^- = 117$ pm). There is a mismatch in sizes with the tetrafluoroborate ion (which actually has a radius of 218 pm). Thus the hydration energy will more probably exceed the (lower) lattice energy, making the compound more soluble.

11.31   There are two possible answers: that there is appreciable covalent bonding in the lithium hydride, thus reducing the Li–H separation, or that the lithium ion is so small that the lattice consists of touching hydride ions with lithium ions "rattling around" in the lattice holes—this is certainly true of lithium iodide.

11.33   LiF and KI.

11.35   Calcium-40 is a "doubly magic" nucleus with filled shells of protons and neutrons.

Chapter 12

THE GROUP 2 ELEMENTS: THE ALKALINE EARTH METALS

Exercises

12.1   (a) $2\ Ca(s) + O_2(g) \rightarrow 2\ CaO(s)$

     (b) $CaCO_3(s) \rightarrow CaO(s) + CO_2(g)$

     (c) $Ca(HCO_3)_2(aq) \rightarrow CaCO_3(s) + H_2O(l) + CO_2(g)$

     (d) $CaO(s) + 3\ C(s) \rightarrow CaC_2(s) + CO(g)$

12.3   (a) Barium; (b) barium.

12.5   Even though there will be a greater increase in entropy when the magnesium chloride lattice vaporizes compared to that of the sodium chloride lattice (three moles of ions instead of two), the higher charge density magnesium ion will cause the water molecules surrounding it during the hydration step to become much more ordered than with the lower charge density sodium ion. It is this significant difference in hydration entropy that causes the considerable difference in solution entropy change.

12.7   They form 2+ ions exclusively and their salts tend to be highly hydrated.

12.9   The commonly accepted explanation is that the beryllium 2+ cation is so small that six water molecules cannot fit around it.

12.11 Rainwater, an aqueous solution of carbon dioxide, percolates into limestone deposits, reacting with the calcium carbonate to give a solution of calcium hydrogen carbonate. The solution flows away, leaving a space that, with continued rain, enlarges to cave size.

$$CaCO_3(s) + CO_2(aq) + H_2O(l) \rightarrow Ca(HCO_3)_2(aq)$$

12.13 Calcium hydroxide is added to seawater, causing precipitation of the less soluble magnesium hydroxide:

$$Ca(OH)_2(aq) + Mg^{2+}(aq) \rightarrow Mg(OH)_2(s) + Ca^{2+}(aq)$$

The magnesium hydroxide is filtered off and neutralized with hydrochloric acid:

$$Mg(OH)_2(s) + 2\ HCl(aq) \rightarrow MgCl_2(aq) + 2\ H_2O(l)$$

The solution is evaporated to dryness and electrolysed:

$$Mg^{2+}(MgCl_2) + 2 e^- \rightarrow Mg(l)$$

$$2 Cl^-(MgCl_2) \rightarrow Cl_2(g) + 2 e^-$$

(It can be added that the chlorine is recycled to produce the hydrochloric acid reagent, while the calcium hydroxide comes from limestone by heating to calcium oxide and adding water.)

12.15   (a) $Ca(OH)_2$ (hydrated lime) or CaO (quicklime); (b) $Mg(OH)_2$;
(c) $MgSO_4 \cdot 7 H_2O$.

12.17   The absorption of X-rays depends on the square of the atomic number of the element. Thus lead is used because it has the highest atomic number of the common, non-radioactive elements (and it is a soft, malleable metal, so it is feasible to make lead aprons and other shields).

12.19   Both metals form tough oxide coatings over their surface that protect the bulk of the metal from oxidation; the two metals are amphoteric, forming beryllate and aluminate anions; they both form carbides containing the C^{4-} ion.

12.21   Magnesium ion is a key component of chlorophyll, the one molecule that has been crucial to converting our planet's atmosphere from carbon dioxide to dioxygen.

12.23   (a) $Mg(s) + HCl(aq) \rightarrow MgCl_2(aq) + H_2(g)$
then evaporate to dryness to crystallize $MgCl_2 \cdot 6 H_2O(s)$.

(b) $Mg(s) + Cl_2(g) \rightarrow MgCl_2(s)$

Beyond the Basics

12.25 $CaSO_4 \cdot 2 H_2O(s) \rightarrow CaSO_4 \cdot \frac{1}{2} H_2O(s) + 1\frac{1}{2} H_2O(g)$

ΔH° $= [1(-1577) + 1\frac{1}{2}(-242) - 1(-2023)]$ kJ·mol^{-1}

    $= +83$ kJ·mol^{-1}

ΔS° $= [1(131) + 1\frac{1}{2}(189) - 1(194)]$ J·mol^{-1}·K^{-1}

    $= +220$ J·mol^{-1}·K^{-1} $= 0.220$ kJ·mol^{-1}·K^{-1}

ΔG° $= (+83$ kJ·mol$^{-1}) - T(+0.220$ kJ·mol^{-1}·K$^{-1}) = 0$

T $= 377$ K $= 104°C$ (close to the actual value of about 100°C)

(If liquid water is used as product, a temperature of 132°C is calculated, which indicates that the value for $H_2O(g)$ has to be used.)

12.27 Except for the second period, most metal ions are hydrated by six water molecules. Thus the formula is actually $[Mg(OH_2)_6]^{2+}[SO_4 \cdot H_2O]^{2-}$. It is also possible to use the analogy with the zinc sulfate heptahydrate formula (Chapter 5).

12.29 BeH^+, as the molecular orbital diagrams show. This ion would possess a single bond, while the neutral molecule would have a half bond and BeH^- would not exist.

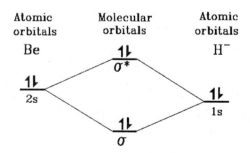

12.31 $Ca_3N_2(s) + 4\ NH_3(l) \rightarrow 3\ Ca(NH_2)_2(NH_3)$

12.33 $BeF_2(s) + Mg(s) \rightarrow MgF_2(s) + Be(s)$

$\Delta G° = [(-1071) - (-979)] \text{ kJ·mol}^{-1} = -92 \text{ kJ·mol}^{-1}$

Less favorable, for at a higher temperature, the low-melting magnesium will be a liquid:

$BeF_2(s) + Mg(l) \rightarrow MgF_2(s) + Be(s)$

Because liquids have higher entropies than solids, there will be a decrease in entropy for the process, and hence as $\Delta G = \Delta H - T\Delta S$, a less-negative free energy change.

The reason for synthesizing at a higher temperature is the greatly increased rate of reaction resulting from the liquid magnesium acting as a "solvent." At room temperature, reaction between two solids will be very slow.

12.35   The species is probably Na_2BeCl_4, containing sodium ions and the tetrahedral tetrachloroberyllate ion, $[BeCl_4]^{2-}$.

Chapter 13

THE GROUP 13 ELEMENTS

Exercises

13.1   (a) $3 K(l) + AlCl_3(s) \rightarrow Al(s) + 3 KCl(s)$

         (b) $B_2O_3(s) + 2 NH_3(g) \rightarrow 2 BN(s) + 3 H_2O(g)$

         (c) $2 Al(s) + 2 OH^-(aq) + 6 H_2O(l) \rightarrow 2 [Al(OH)_4]^-(aq) + 3 H_2(g)$

         (d) $2 B_4H_{10}(g) + 11 O_2(g) \rightarrow 4 B_2O_3(s) + 10 H_2O(g)$

13.3   The bridging oxygen atoms have an oxidation number of -1:

13.5 $B_2H_7^-$ corresponds to the generic formula $[B_nH_{n+5}]^-$. Thus it is the simplest *arachno*-cluster.

13.7   See the energy cycle diagram. The major factors in the very large enthalpy of formation are the weak fluorine-fluorine bond, the weakest of the halogen bonds; and the exceedingly strong boron-fluorine bond (the latter can be explained as either a result of partial ionic character of the very polar B–F bond or some degree of π-orbital formation involving a full $2p$ orbital of the fluorine and an empty $2p$ orbital of the boron).

13.9   In the hexahydrate ion, the Al^{3+} is surrounded by the partially negative oxygen atoms of the six water molecules, with the partially positive hydrogens of the water molecules pointing away from the ion. In effect, then, the charge is delocalized over the whole hydrated ion rather than being concentrated in the small Al^{3+} "core."

13.11   The hydrated aluminum ion acts as a Bronsted-Lowry acid in the following way:

$$[Al(OH_2)_6]^{3+}(aq) + H_2O(l) \rightarrow H_3O^+(aq) + [Al(OH_2)_5(OH)]^{2+}(aq)$$

13.13   The potential environmental hazards are "red mud"—the basic residue from the bauxite purification; hydrogen fluoride gas from hydrolysis of cryolite; the carbon oxides that are produced at the anode; and fluorocarbon compounds produced by reaction of fluorine with the carbon anode.

13.15   Aluminum fluoride is a typical ionic compound with a high melting point. Both aluminum bromide and aluminum iodide are covalently bonded dimers, Al_2Br_6 and Al_2I_6. Aluminum chloride is a borderline case: in the solid, it has an ionic structure that can alternatively be considered as network covalent, while in the liquid phase, it consists of covalently bonded dimers, Al_2Cl_6.

13.17   A spinel has the formula AB_2X_4, where A is a dipositive metal ion, B is a tripositive metal ion, and X is a dinegative ion. The negative ion forms a cubic close-packed arrangement, and in the normal spinel, the A cations occupy tetrahedral sites and the B cations octahedral sites. In the reverse spinel, the A cations occupy octahedral sites while half of the B cations occupy the tetrahedral sites, the other half octahedral sites.

13.19   Gallium(III) fluoride must consist of an ionic lattice of gallium(3+) and chloride(1−) ions while gallium(III) chloride must contain discrete $GaCl_3$ molecules.

13.21   Aluminum ion forms the highly insoluble aluminum hydroxide in neutral conditions. However, in acid conditions, such as lakes acidified by acid rain, the soluble $Al(OH_2)_6^{3+}$ is produced. The aluminum ion is very toxic to fish.

Beyond the Basics

13.23 The metallic radius is a measure of the atomic size when packed in a metal crystal lattice. It will not be much smaller than the van der Waals (nonbonding) radius. The covalent radius will be smaller because there is orbital overlap with the atom to which it is covalently bonded. The ionic radius is by far the smallest because all the valence electrons have been lost and the measure is simply of the core of the ion.

13.25 $Cl_3Al[O(C_2H_5)_2]$, where a lone pair on the oxygen of the ether occupies the fourth bonding site around the aluminum ion.

13.27 As we might expect from the diagonal relationship (Chapter 9), the beryllium ion will resemble the aluminum ion. Hence:
$$[Be(OH_2)_4]^{2+}(aq) + H_2O(l) \rightarrow [Be(OH_2)_3(OH)]^+(aq) + H_3O^+(aq)$$

13.29 Let number of ions of magnesium $= x$, then:
$$1 \times (K^+) + x \times (Mg^{2+}) + 1 \times (Al^{3+}) + 3 \times (Si^{4+}) + 10 \times (O^{2-}) + 2 \times (OH^-)$$
$$= 0$$
$$1(+1) + x(+2) + 1(+3) + 3(+4) + 10(-2) + 2(-1) = 0$$
$$x = +3.$$

13.31 Setting up the disproportionation reaction:
$$3\ GaCl(s) \rightarrow GaCl_3(s) + 2\ Ga(s)$$
$$\Delta H = \Sigma \Delta H_f^\circ(\text{products}) - \Sigma \Delta H_f^\circ(\text{reactants})$$
$$= [1(-525) + 2(0)] - [1(+38)] = -563\ kJ \cdot mol^{-1}$$
Because there are equal moles (in the same phase) on each side of the equation, the free energy for the disproportionation should be equally high. Thus disproportionation should occur.

13.33 $4\ AlCl_3(s) + CH_3CN(l) \rightarrow [Al(CH_3CN)_6]^{3+}(CH_3CN) + 3\ [AlCl_4]^-(CH_3CN)$

13.35 $Ga(OH_2)_6^{3+}(aq) \rightarrow GaO(OH)(s) + H_2O(l) + 3\ H_3O^+(aq)$
Addition of acid (hydronium ion) will shift the equilibrium to the left.

13.37   Aluminum, lacking any "inner" *d* electrons, behaves more like a Group 3
        element than a Group 13 element. Thus its hydride is more likely to
        resemble that of scandium. The hydride of gallium follows from that of
        boron in being a small-molecule covalent dimer. [in fact, the scandium
        hydrides are ionic, thus aluminum being network covalent would fit well
        above it]

13.39

13.41   We can calculate the B–H bridging bond energy by means of an energy
        diagram. The bond formation can be divided into two steps: the formation
        of four B–H terminal bonds and the formation of four B–H bridging bonds
        (see below). When we do this, a value of 208 kJ·mol^{-1} per mole of B–H
        bridging bonds is obtained almost exactly half the value of the 389
        kJ·mol^{-1} of a normal B–H bond. This fits well with the concept of a single
        bonding pair shared by the two bonds.

13.43 $B_2H_6(g) + 3\ O_2(g) \rightarrow B_2O_3(s) + 3\ H_2O(l)$

          $\Delta H_{comb}(C_2H_6) = \Delta H_f(B_2O_3) + 3 \times \Delta H_f(H_2O) - \Delta H_f(B_2H_6)$

          $[(-2165) = \Delta H_f(B_2O_3) + 3(-286) - (+36)]\ kJ \cdot mol^{-1}$

          $\Delta H_f(B_2O_3) = -1271\ kJ \cdot mol^{-1}$

13.45   For sodium chloride packing, the radius ratio r_+/r_- must be between 0.414 and 0.732.

        From the icosahedral structure of B_{12} (Figure 13.1), the radius of the boron cluster would seem to be about the sum of two atoms, 176 pm. If we assume the zirconium(IV) ion, this would give a radius ratio of about 0.41, essentially what could be expected to form an NaCl lattice. Using the atomic radius of zirconium would give a ratio of sizes of close to unity: not what one would expect for an NaCl packing pattern. The structure must be $[Zr^{4+}][B_{12}^{4-}]$.

Chapter 14

THE GROUP 14 ELEMENTS

Exercises

14.1   (a) $Li_2C_2(s) + 2\,H_2O(l) \rightarrow 2\,LiOH(aq) + C_2H_2(g)$

      (b) $SiO_2(s) + 2\,C(s) \rightarrow Si(l) + 2\,CO(g)$

      (c) $CuO(s) + CO(g) \rightarrow Cu(s) + CO_2(g)$

      (d) $Ca(OH)_2(aq) + CO_2(g) \rightarrow CaCO_3(s) + H_2O(l)$

             $CaCO_3(s) + CO_2(g) + H_2O(l) \rightarrow Ca(HCO_3)_2(aq)$

      (e) $CH_4(g) + 4\,S(l) \rightarrow CS_2(g) + 2\,H_2S(g)$

      (f) $SiO_2(s) + 2\,Na_2CO_3(l) \rightarrow Na_4SiO_4(s) + 2\,CO_2(g)$

      (g) $PbO_2(s) + 4\,HCl(aq) \rightarrow PbCl_4(aq) + 2\,H_2O(l)$

             $PbCl_4(aq) \rightarrow PbCl_2(s) + Cl_2(g)$

14.3   (a) The ability of an element to form chains of its atoms.

      (b) Silicates in which there are numerous cavities in the structure resulting in very low densities.

      (c) Non-metallic inorganic compounds prepared by high temperature synthesis.

      (d) Chains of alternating silicon and oxygen atoms to which organic (carbon-containing) side groups are attached.

14.5   Diamond is a very hard, transparent, colorless solid that is a good conductor of heat but a non-conductor of electricity. It is insoluble in all solvents and it is chemically unreactive except upon heating in dioxygen. Graphite is a soft, slippery, black solid that is a poor conductor of heat but a good conductor of electricity. It is insoluble in all solvents and will react chemically with only very reactive elements such as dioxygen and difluorine. C_{60} is black and a nonconductor of heat and electricity. It is soluble in many nonpolar and low-polarity solvents and it is quite reactive chemically.

14.7   Diamond and graphite both have network covalent bonded structures. The solvation process cannot provide the energy necessary to break nonpolar covalent bonds. The fullerenes consist of discrete molecules, such as C_{60}.

These individual nonpolar units can become solvated by nonpolar or low-polarity solvent molecules and hence dissolve.

14.9   The three classes are ionic, covalent, and metallic. Ionic carbides are formed by the most electropositive metals. These may contain the dicarbide(2–) ion, C_2^{2-}, or the true carbide ion C^{4-}. Both types of ionic carbides react with water to produce the appropriate hydrocarbon. Covalent carbides are formed by nonmetals, specifically boron and silicon, more electronegative than carbon. These carbides are very hard and have high melting points. The metallic carbides are interstitial carbides, in that the carbon atoms fit in interstices within the metal structure. As such, they have many metallic properties, such as hardness, metallic luster, and electrical conductivity.

14.11   The chemical equation is

$$SiO_2(s) + 3\ C(s) \rightarrow SiC(s) + 2\ CO(g)$$

and with the net increase of two moles of gas, the reaction should be entropy driven. The need for high-temperature synthesis might indicate that there is not only a high activation energy but also the possibility of the reaction being endothermic (according to Le Chatelier's principle).

$\Delta H°$ $= [1(-65) + 2(-111) - 1(-911) - 3(0)] \text{ kJ·mol}^{-1}$

$= +624 \text{ kJ·mol}^{-1}$

$\Delta S°$ $= [1(+17) + 2(+198) - 1(+41) - 3(6)] \text{ J·mol}^{-1}\text{·K}^{-1}$

$= +354 \text{ J·mol}^{-1}\text{·K}^{-1} = +0.354 \text{ kJ·mol}^{-1}\text{·K}^{-1}$

Thus there is indeed a substantial increase in entropy (the driving force for the reaction), while the reaction is also very endothermic.

$\Delta G°$ $= (+624 \text{ kJ·mol}^{-1}) - (2273 \text{ K})(+0.354 \text{ kJ·mol}^{-1}\text{·K}^{-1})$

$= -181 \text{ kJ·mol}^{-1}$

At this temperature the reaction is spontaneous.

14.13   As can be seen from the enthalpy of the following formation diagrams, it is the lower bond energy of the C=S bond compared to the C=O bond that makes such a large difference in the enthalpy of formation values.

14.15   Because the central carbon atom must form two σ bonds to the sulfur atoms, we assume that *sp* hybrid orbitals are formed. Like carbon dioxide, we consider that the 2*p* orbitals at right angles to the *sp* hybrid orbitals overlap with 3*p* orbitals of the sulfur to provide a pair of π bonds.

14.17   We explain the high activation energy of methane in terms of the lack of any empty orbitals on the carbon atoms that can be used for intermediate formation in the oxidation process. Silicon in the comparable silane molecule has empty $3d$ orbitals that can be involved in the oxidation process.

14.19   The synthesis of HFC-134a requires a complex, expensive multistep procedure. Also, higher pressures are necessary for its liquefaction, compared with the CFCs, making it necessary to completely replace the old refrigeration units when changing to HFC-134a.

14.21   Methane is a particularly potent greenhouse gas because it absorbs wavelengths in the infrared region that are currently transparent.

14.23   This ion is isoelectronic with nitrogen dioxide. It has a single unpaired electron, so the bond angle is greater than 120°. The bond order would be about 1½ compared to 2 in carbon dioxide.

$$\left[\; \ddot{\mathrm{O}} :: \mathrm{C} \; \overset{\textstyle \cdot}{} \; \underset{\textstyle :\ddot{\mathrm{O}}:}{} \; \right]^{-}$$

14.25   Trigonal planar, because there appear to be three bonding directions around the central carbon. This would be one of three possible resonance structures resulting in an extended π-bond system throughout the ion. The average carbon-carbon bond order is $1\frac{1}{3}$.

$$\left[:\mathrm{N} ::: \mathrm{C} : \underset{\underset{\displaystyle :\ddot{\mathrm{N}}:}{\overset{\displaystyle ::}{\underset{\displaystyle \mathrm{C}}{\overset{\displaystyle ::}{}}}}{\mathrm{C}} : \mathrm{C} ::: \mathrm{N}: \right]^{-}$$

14.27 Because the Si_4O_{11} unit has a charge of 6–, for neutrality in the compound the five iron ions must have a total charge of 12+. If the number of Fe^{2+} ions is x and the number of Fe^{3+} ions is y, we can say:

$$x(+2) + y(+3) = +12$$

but $(x + y) = 5$, the sum of the iron ions. Hence by substitution, $x = 3$ and $y = 2$. Thus there are three Fe^{2+} ions and two Fe^{3+} ions per formula.

14.29 Zeolites are used as ion exchangers for water; as adsorption agents, particularly for water in organic solvents; for gas separation, particularly dioxygen and dinitrogen from air; and most important, as specialized catalysts, particularly in the oil industry.

14.31 Silicone polymers are very stable chemically. Thus any polymer molecules that leak from the plastic sac in breast implants cannot be broken down by normal bodily processes.

14.33 Electron-dot structures of tin(IV) chloride and tin(II) chloride:

(a)   (b)

The corresponding molecular shapes (tetrahedral and V-shaped) according to VSEPR theory:

(a)   (b)

14.35 The half-equations are:

$$PbO(s) + H_2O(l) \rightarrow PbO_2(s) + 2\ H^+(aq) + 2\ e^-$$
$$PbO(s) + 2\ H^+(aq) + 2\ e^- \rightarrow Pb(s) + H_2O(l)$$

14.37 CN^- and CO are the most common species isoelectronic with C_2^{2-}.

14.39   The major problem with inorganic polymer chemistry is the lack of the range of synthetic pathways compared with those available for organic polymer synthesis.

14.41   Carbon:

$4\ CO(g) + Ni(s) \rightarrow Ni(CO)_4(g)$

$CO(g) + Cl_2(g) \rightarrow COCl_2(g)$

$CO(g) + S(s) \rightarrow COS(g)$

$HCOOH(l) \xrightarrow{H_2SO_4} CO(g) + H_2O(l)$

$CO_2(g) + 2\ Ca(s) \rightarrow C(s) + 2\ CaO(s)$

$2\ CO(g) + O_2(g) \rightarrow 2\ CO_2(g)$

$CO(g) + 2\ H_2(g) \xrightarrow{catalyst} CH_3OH(l)$

$2\ C(s) + O_2(g) \rightarrow 2\ CO(g)$

$C(s) + O_2(g) \rightarrow CO_2(g)$

$Na_2C_2(s) + 2\ H_2O(l) \rightarrow 2\ NaOH(aq) + C_2H_2(g)$

$2\ C_2H_2(g) + 5\ O_2(g) \rightarrow 4\ CO_2(g) + 2\ H_2O(l)$

$Al_4C_3(s) + H_2O(l) \rightarrow 3\ CH_4(g) + 4\ Al(OH)_3(s)$

$CH_4(g) + 2\ O_2(g) \rightarrow CO_2(g) + 2\ H_2O(l)$

$CH_4(g) + 4\ S(l) \rightarrow CS_2(g) + 2\ H_2S(g)$

$CS_2(g) + 3\ Cl_2(g) \rightarrow CCl_4(g) + S_2Cl_2(l)$

$CS_2(g) + S_2Cl_2(l) \rightarrow CCl_4(g) + 6\ S(s)$

$CH_4(g) + NH_3(g) \rightarrow HCN(g) + 3\ H_2(g)$

$HCN(aq) + H_2O(l) \rightarrow H_3O^+(aq) + CN^-(aq)$

$Ca(OH)_2(aq) + CO_2(g) \rightarrow CaCO_3(s) + H_2O(l)$

$CaCO_3(s) + 2\ HCl(aq) \rightarrow CaCl_2(aq) + H_2O(l) + CO_2(g)$

$CaCO_3(s) + H_2O(l) + CO_2(g) \rightarrow Ca(HCO_3)_2(aq)$

Silicon:

$Si(s) + HCl(g) \rightarrow SiHCl_3(g) + H_2(g)$

$2\ CH_3Cl(g) + Si(s) \rightarrow (CH_3)_2SiCl_2(l)$

$SiO_2(s) + 2\ C(s) \rightarrow Si(s) + 2\ CO(g)$

$SiO_2(s) + 6\ HF(aq) \rightarrow SiF_6^{2-}(aq) + 2\ H^+(aq) + 2\ H_2O(l)$

$SiO_2(s) + 2\ NaOH(l) \rightarrow Na_2SiO_3(s) + H_2O(g)$

$SiO_2(s) + 3\ C(s) \rightarrow SiC(s) + 2\ CO(g)$

$SiO_2(s) + 2\ Na_2CO_3(l) \xrightarrow{\Delta} Na_4SiO_4(s) + 2\ CO_2(g)$

$2\ SiO_4^{4-}(aq) + 2\ H^+(aq) \rightarrow Si_2O_7^{6-}(aq) + H_2O(l)$

Beyond the Basics

14.43 Lead(II) ion has a similar charge density to that of the calcium ion. Thus it will readily replace calcium ion in the bone structure.

14.45 At high temperatures, the sodium and calcium ions can leach out of the glass structure. This will result in the loss of transparency.

14.47 (a) A six-membered ring structure, Si_3O_3, with alternating silicon and oxygen atoms. Each silicon atom has two singly bonded oxygen atoms attached to it.

(b) $P_3O_9^{3-}$

(c) S_3O_9. In fact, this is the common form of sulfur trioxide; see Chapter 16.

14.49 Tin(II) chloride is the Lewis acid because it is an electron pair acceptor, while the chloride ion, the Lewis base, is an electron pair donor.

14.51 $Mg_2SiO_4(s) + 2\ \text{"}H_2CO_3(aq)\text{"} \rightarrow 2\ MgCO_3(s) + SiO_2(s) + 2\ H_2O(l)$

14.53 $A = CH_4; B = S; C = CS_2; D = H_2S; E = Cl_2; F = CCl_4$

$CH_4(g) + 4\ S(s) \rightarrow CS_2(g) + 2\ H_2S(g)$

$CS_2(g) + 2\ Cl_2(g) \rightarrow CCl_4(g) + 2\ S(s)$

$CH_4(g) + 4\ Cl_2(g) \rightarrow CCl_4(g) + 4\ HCl(g)$

14.55   To solve this problem, we need to assume that the ethyl, C_2H_5, unit remains intact. For compound Y,

$$\text{mol Sn} = 0.1240 \text{ g} \times \frac{1 \text{ mol SnO}_2}{150.5 \text{ g}} \times \frac{1 \text{ mol Sn}}{1 \text{ mol SnO}_2} = 8.239 \times 10^{-4} \text{ mol Sn}$$

We can convert to the mass of tin and subtract from the mass of compound, find the mass of ethyl units, and then determine moles. Alternatively, we can find the molar mass of the compound (assuming it contains one tin), subtract the molar mass of tin, and then determine the number of ethyl units. The latter method will be used here.

$$\text{molar mass Y} = \frac{0.1935 \text{ g}}{8.239 \times 10^{-4} \text{ mol}} = 234.9 \text{ g} \cdot \text{mol}^{-1}$$

$$234.9 \text{ g·mol}^{-1} = [118.7 + n(29.0)] \text{ g·mol}^{-1}$$
$$n = 4.00$$

Thus the formula of Y is $Sn(C_2H_5)_4$

For compound Z, we will first work out the mass of tin(IV) oxide and silver chloride produced from 1.000 g of Z.

Mass SnO_2 = (0.1164 g)/(0.1865 g Z) = 0.6241 g

Mass AgCl = (0.1332 g)/(0.2240 g Z) = 0.5946 g

$$\text{mol Sn} = 0.6241 \text{ g} \times \frac{1 \text{ mol SnO}_2}{150.5 \text{ g}} \times \frac{1 \text{ mol Sn}}{1 \text{ mol SnO}_2} \times \frac{118.7 \text{ g}}{1 \text{ mol Sn}} = 0.4922 \text{ g Sn}$$

$$\text{mol Cl} = 0.5946 \text{ g} \times \frac{1 \text{ mol AgCl}}{143.4 \text{ g}} \times \frac{1 \text{ mol Cl}}{1 \text{ mol AgCl}} \times \frac{35.45 \text{ g}}{1 \text{ mol Cl}} = 0.1470 \text{ g Cl}$$

Mass C_2H_5 = 1.000 g – 0.4922 g – 0.1470 g = 0.3608 g C_2H_5.

$$\text{mole ratios} = \frac{0.4922 \text{ g Sn}}{118.7 \text{ g} \cdot \text{mol}^{-1}} : \frac{0.1470 \text{ g Cl}}{35.45 \text{ g} \cdot \text{mol}^{-1}} : \frac{0.3608 \text{ g C}_2\text{H}_5}{29.04 \text{ g} \cdot \text{mol}^{-1}}$$

$$= 4.147 \times 10^{-3} \text{ mol Sn} : 4.147 \times 10^{-3} \text{ mol Cl} : 1.242 \times 10^{-2} \text{ mol C}_2\text{H}_5$$

$$= 1 \text{ Sn} : 1 \text{ Cl} : 3 \text{ C}_2\text{H}_5$$

Thus the formula of Z is $SnCl(C_2H_5)_3$

Equation for the reaction:

$3 Sn(C_2H_5)_4(l) + SnCl_4(l) \rightarrow 4 SnCl(C_2H_5)_3(l)$

This is also compatible with the information that 1.41 g of Y reacts with 0.52 g of tin(IV) chloride to give 1.93 g of Z, since the mass of Z being the sum of the masses of the reactants means there is no other product.

14.57   First we need the values for $\Delta H°$ and $\Delta S°$ of $Ca(HCO_3)_2$, which we can find by summing the values for the individual ions:

$\Delta H° = [(-543) + 2(-690)] \text{ kJ·mol}^{-1} = -1923 \text{ kJ·mol}^{-1}$

$\Delta S° = [(-56) + 2(+98)] \text{ J·mol}^{-1}\text{·K}^{-1} = +140 \text{ J·mol}^{-1}\text{·K}^{-1}$

Now we can find ΔH and ΔS for the reaction:

$\Delta H° = [(-1923) - (-1207) - (-394) - (-286)] \text{ kJ·mol}^{-1} = -36 \text{ kJ·mol}^{-1}$

$\Delta S° = [(+140) - (+93) - (+214) - (+70)] \text{ J·mol}^{-1}\text{·K}^{-1} = -237 \text{ J·mol}^{-1}\text{·K}^{-1}$

At 80°C:

$\Delta G° = -36 \text{ kJ·mol}^{-1} - (353 \text{ K})(-0.237 \text{ J·mol}^{-1}\text{·K}^{-1}) = +48 \text{ kJ·mol}^{-1}$

A positive value indicates that the decomposition reaction will be favored.

14.59   Bonds in C_2O_4 = 1(C–C) + 1(O–O) + 2(C=C) + 2(C–O)

$= [1(346) + 1(142) + 2(799) + 2(358)] \text{ kJ·mol}^{-1}$

$= 2802 \text{ kJ·mol}^{-1}$

Bonds in $2CO_2$ = 4(C=O)

$= [4(799)] \text{ kJ·mol}^{-1} = 3196 \text{ kJ·mol}^{-1}$

Energy released = $[3196 - 2802] \text{ kJ·mol}^{-1} = 394 \text{ kJ·mol}^{-1}$

Chapter 15

THE GROUP 15 ELEMENTS

Exercises

15.1 (a) $AsCl_3(l) + 3 H_2O(l) \rightarrow H_3AsO_3(aq) + 3 HCl(g)$

     (b) $3 Mg(s) + N_2(g) \rightarrow Mg_3N_2(s)$

     (c) $NH_3(g) + 3 Cl_2(g) \rightarrow NCl_3(l) + 3 HCl(g)$

     (d) $CH_4(g) + H_2O(g) \rightarrow CO(g) + 3 H_2(g)$

     (e) $N_2H_4(l) + O_2(g) \rightarrow N_2(g) + 2 H_2O(g)$

     (f) $NH_4NO_3(aq) \rightarrow N_2O(g) + 2 H_2O(l)$

     (g) $2 NaOH(aq) + N_2O_3(aq) \rightarrow 2 NaNO_2(aq) + H_2O(l)$

     (h) $2 NaNO_3(s) \rightarrow 2 NaNO_2(s) + O_2(g)$

     (i) $P_4O_{10}(g) + C(s) \rightarrow P_4(g) + 10 CO(g)$

15.3   Arsenic has both metallic and nonmetallic allotropes; its oxides are amphoteric, while its chemistry mostly resembles nonmetallic phosphorus.

15.5   The first point of contrast is the difference in boiling points: the nonpolar hydrocarbons have very low boiling points, while the hydrogen-bonding hydrides of nitrogen have much higher boiling points. Following from this, they have different acid-base properties, both hydrides of carbon being neutral while those of nitrogen are basic:

$$NH_3(aq) + H_2O(l) \rightarrow NH_4^+(aq) + OH^-(aq)$$
$$N_2H_4(aq) + H_2O(l) \rightarrow N_2H_5^+(aq) + OH^-(aq)$$

The most obvious difference is in their combustions, both hydrocarbons producing carbon dioxide while the nitrogen hydrides produce nitrogen gas:

$$CH_4(g) + 2 O_2(g) \rightarrow CO_2(g) + 2 H_2O(g)$$
$$2 C_2H_4(g) + 6 O_2(g) \rightarrow 4 CO_2(g) + 4 H_2O(g)$$
$$4 NH_3(g) + 3 O_2(g) \rightarrow 2 N_2(g) + 6 H_2O(g)$$
$$N_2H_4(l) + O_2(g) \rightarrow N_2(g) + 2 H_2O(l)$$

15.7   (a) Nitrogen has a very strong nitrogen-nitrogen triple bond; hence any reaction that produces dinitrogen will have a strongly negative enthalpy contribution even before the other terms in the energy cycle are included.

Also, being a gas, its formation will contribute a positive factor to the entropy change.

(b) Though dinitrogen is often the thermodynamically preferred product, kinetic factors (that is, comparative activation energies) can lead to other products.

15.9   Air contains about 1 percent argon. Thus as the unreacted gases are recycled and additional air is added, the argon proportion will continuously increase. One possibility would be to cool the mixture and have the argon condense out, since it has a boiling point higher than dinitrogen or dihydrogen. However, the energy requirements for this procedure would probably be prohibitive. Alternatively, the used gases could be periodically siphoned off and the dihydrogen burned as an energy source.

15.11   Though the ammonium ion is very similar to an alkali metal ion in terms of charge density (thus stabilizing large, low-charge anions) and compound solubility, it has two major differences. First, a solution of the ion is acidic, not neutral, due to the following equilibrium:

$$NH_4^+(aq) + H_2O(l) \rightarrow H_3O^+(aq) + NH_3(aq)$$

Second, its compounds are all very thermally unstable, unlike those of the alkali metal ions, and the products are quite dissimilar. For example, ammonium nitrate decomposes on gentle heating to give dinitrogen oxide and water, while sodium nitrate upon very strong heating forms sodium nitrite and dioxygen:

$$NH_4NO_3(s) \rightarrow N_2O(g) + 2\ H_2O(g)$$
$$2\ NaNO_3(s) \rightarrow 2\ NaNO_2(s) + O_2(g)$$

15.13   The least formal charge is provided by the following representation of two double bonds:

$$: \ddot{N} :: N :: \ddot{N} :$$
$$\ominus \quad \oplus \quad \ominus$$

15.15   The chemical equation is

$$2 \ NaN_3(s) \rightarrow 2 \ Na(s) + 3 \ N_2(g)$$

Mole of $NaN_3 = 7.7 \times 10^{-2}$ mol

Mole of $N_2 = 0.11(5)$ mol

Volume of gas = nRT/P

$$= (0.115 \ mol)(8.31 \ kPa \cdot L \cdot mol^{-1} \cdot K^{-1})(298K)/(102 \ kPa)$$

$$= 2.8 \ L$$

15.17   It is ammonia that has the "anomolous" boiling point as a result of the strong hydrogen bonds between neighboring ammonia molecules.

15.19   The shapes are:

(a)   (b)   (c)   (d)

15.21   The reaction

$$2 \ NO(g) + O_2(g) \rightarrow 2 \ NO_2(g)$$

is performed under high pressure because the reaction direction is favored that will result in the lesser moles of gas. A low temperature will increase the yield, as the forward process is exothermic. Both conclusions are in accordance with Le Chatelier's principle.

15.23   White phosphorus is a very reactive, white, waxy substance that consists of P_4 molecules, shown in (a), while red phosphorus is a red powdery solid that consists of long polymer chains of linked P_4 units, shown in (b). White phosphorus burns in contact with the oxygen in air, while red is air-stable. The white allotrope melts in hot water and is very soluble in nonpolar solvents, while the red allotrope is high melting and is insoluble in all solvents.

(a)   (b)

15.25   Because ammonia acts as a proton acceptor when phosphine is dissolved in it, ammonia must be the stronger base. Conversely, as phosphine acts as a proton donor, it must be a less strong base (and thus a stronger acid).

15.27   The oxidation number of nitrogen is +3, and the N–O bond order is 2:

-1   +3   -2

The chemical reaction is:

$$\tfrac{1}{2}\,N_2(g) + \tfrac{1}{2}\,O_2(g) + \tfrac{1}{2}\,Cl_2(g) \rightarrow NOCl(g)$$

Using bond energy values from the Appendix:

Bonds broken:	½(N–N)	= ½(942) kJ	= 471 kJ
	½(O=O)	= ½(494) kJ	= 247 kJ
	½(Cl–Cl)	= ½(240) kJ	= 120 kJ
		Total	= 838 kJ
Bonds formed:	1(N–Cl)	= 1(313) kJ	= 313 kJ
	1(N–O)	= 1(N–O) kJ	= N–O kJ

Net energy change = 53 kJ   = [838 – 313 – (N–O)] kJ

(N–O) = 472 kJ

The average values for single and double nitrogen-oxygen bonds are 201 kJ and 607 kJ. On this basis, the bond order is approaching that of a double bond (we have assumed that the N–Cl bond does have the typical single-bond value).

15.29   Following is the electron-dot structure and molecular shape of P_2Cl_4.

$$\begin{array}{c}
:\!\overset{\cdot\cdot}{\underset{}{Cl}}\!: \\[-2pt]
:\!\overset{\cdot\cdot}{\underset{\cdot\cdot}{Cl}}\!:\overset{\cdot\cdot}{P}:\overset{\cdot\cdot}{P}:\overset{\cdot\cdot}{\underset{\cdot\cdot}{Cl}}\!: \\[-2pt]
:\!\overset{}{\underset{\cdot\cdot}{Cl}}\!:
\end{array}$$

15.31 The bromine atom is probably too large for six of them to be accommodated around a phosphorus atom.

15.33 In hydrogen azide, formal charge arguments would give an equal weighting to the double-double and single-triple nitrogen-nitrogen bonds. As can be seen from figure (a), for the azide ion, the double-double nitrogen-nitrogen bond is strongly preferred.

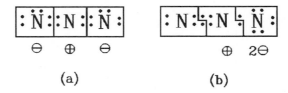

(a)   (b)

15.35 Half reactions:

$NH_2OH(aq) + 2 H_2O(l) \rightarrow NO_3^-(aq) + 7 H^+(aq) + 6 e^-$

$BrO_3^-(aq) + 6 H^+(aq) + 6 e^- \rightarrow Br^-(aq) + 3 H_2O(l)$

Overall reaction:

$NH_2OH(aq) + BrO_3^-(aq) \rightarrow NO_3^-(aq) + Br^-(aq) + H_3O^+(aq)$

15.37 $NOF(g) + SbF_5(l) \rightarrow NO^+(SbF_5) + SbF_6^-(SbF_5)$

15.39 $H_2S_2O_7$ and $H_6Si_2O_7$.

15.41 (a) Rapid algae growth leading to a depletion of dissolved dioxygen in lakes and rivers.

(b) Mutually beneficial relationship between two organisms.

(c) Use of a chemical compound to combat disease.

(d) Geological name of calcium hydroxide phosphate that is the bone material.

Beyond the Basics

15.43   The initial products are PH_4^+ and Cl^- (analogous to ammonia). The chloride ion then reacts with the electron-pair acceptor BCl_3 to give BCl_4^-.

$PH_3(g) + HCl(l) \rightarrow PH_4^+(HCl) + Cl^-(HCl)$

$Cl^-(HCl) + BCl_3(HCl) \rightarrow BCl_4^-(HCl)$

In the first reaction, phosphine is the Lewis base, hydrogen chloride the Lewis acid. In the second reaction, it is the chloride ion that is the base; boron trichloride is the acid.

15.45   There are two alternatives, one with the single electron in a bond, the other with it on the double-bonded oxygen. In both cases, the bond angles should all be 120°. The average bond order would be 1.33 in the first case and 1.17 in the other.

15.47   The most obvious structure would be that in which the four terminal oxygen atoms in P_4O_{10} are replaced by sulfur atoms.

15.49   The bonding between sodium and azide ions is likely to be predominantly ionic whereas that in the heavy metal azides (Fajan's rules) will be more covalent. It is the covalently bonded species, like hydrogen azide, that are more of an explosion hazard.

15.51   (a) $\ln K = -\dfrac{\Delta G^\circ}{RT} = -\dfrac{-16 \times 10^3 \text{ J} \cdot \text{mol}^{-1}}{8.31 \text{ J} \cdot \text{mol}^{-1} \cdot \text{K}^{-1} \times 298 \text{ K}} = +6.5$

   $K = 6 \times 10^2$

   (b) $\tfrac{1}{2} N_2(g) + \tfrac{3}{2} H_2(g) \rightarrow NH_3(g)$

   $\Delta H^\circ = -46 \text{ kJ} \cdot \text{mol}^{-1}$

   $\Delta S^\circ = [(+193) - \tfrac{1}{2}(+192) - \tfrac{3}{2}(+131)] \text{ J} \cdot \text{mol}^{-1} \cdot \text{K}^{-1}$

   $= -100 \text{ J} \cdot \text{mol}^{-1} \cdot \text{K}^{-1}$

   $\Delta G^\circ = \Delta H^\circ - T\Delta S^\circ = -46 \text{ kJ} \cdot \text{mol}^{-1} - (775 \text{ K})(-0.100 \text{ kJ} \cdot \text{mol}^{-1} \cdot \text{K}^{-1})$

   $= +32 \text{ kJ} \cdot \text{mol}^{-1}$

   $\ln K = -\dfrac{+32 \times 10^3 \text{ J} \cdot \text{mol}^{-1}}{8.31 \text{ J} \cdot \text{mol}^{-1} \cdot \text{K}^{-1} \times 775 \text{ K}} = -5.0$

   $K = 7 \times 10^{-3}$

   (c)   The rate of the reaction is as important as the yield. By performing the reaction at a higher temperature, equilibrium is attained much more rapidly.

15.53 $2 NO_2(g) \rightarrow N_2O_4(g)$

   $\Delta H^\circ = [(+9) - 2(+33)] \text{ kJ} \cdot \text{mol}^{-1} = -57 \text{ kJ} \cdot \text{mol}^{-1}$

   Thus the N–N bond energy must be approximately 57 kJ·mol^{-1}, assuming that the N–O bond strength remains the same.

15.55   The easiest way of solving the problem is to use the Henderson-Hasselbach equation that you should recall from your general chemistry courses:

   $pH = pK_a + \log_{10} \dfrac{[\text{base}]}{[\text{acid}]}$

   Let x = concentration of acid ion; then $(0.10 - x)$ = concentration of base ion.

$$6.80 = 7.21 + \log\frac{(0.10 - x)}{x}$$

$x = [\text{acid}] = 0.072 \text{ mol}\cdot\text{L}^{-1}$, $[\text{base}] = 0.028 \text{ mol}\cdot\text{L}^{-1}$

Mass $Na_2HPO_4 = 4.0$ g, mass $NaH_2PO_4 = 8.6$ g

15.57   The comparable bond energies ($kJ\cdot mol^{-1}$) are shown below:

P–Cl 326	Cl–Cl 240
P–F 490	F–F 155

Assuming that the P–Cl bond has about the same energy in PCl_5 and PCl_3, the dissociation energy is

$[240 - 2(326)] \text{ kJ}\cdot\text{mol}^{-1} = 412 \text{ kJ}\cdot\text{mol}^{-1}$,

a significant amount of energy, but entropy will favor decomposition at high enough temperatures.

For the decomposition of PF_5, the energy change will be

$[155 - 2(490)] \text{ kJ}\cdot\text{mol}^{-1} = 825 \text{ kJ}\cdot\text{mol}^{-1}$.

This much higher value results from fluorine bonds to other elements being stronger than those of chlorine to the same element, and the weakness of the F–F bond compared to the Cl–Cl bond.

15.59 $[NF_4]^+F^-$ — tetrafluoroammonium fluoride.

15.61   [A] Red phosphorus; [B] white phosphorus; [C] tetraphosphorus decaoxide;

[D] phosphoric acid; [E] phosphorus trichloride; [F] phosphorus pentachloride; [G] phosphorous/phosphonic acid.

$4 P(s) \rightarrow P_4(s)$

$P_4(s) + 5 O_2(g) \rightarrow P_4O_{10}(s)$

$P_4O_{10}(s) + 6 H_2O(l) \rightarrow 4 H_3PO_4(aq)$

$P_4(s) + 6 Cl_2(g) \rightarrow 4 PCl_3(l)$

$PCl_3(l) + Cl_2(g) \rightarrow PCl_5(s)$

$PCl_5(s) + 4 H_2O(l) \rightarrow H_3PO_4(aq) + 5 HCl(g)$

$PCl_3(l) + 3 H_2O(l) \rightarrow H_3PO_3(aq) + 3 HCl(g)$

15.63 $Li_3N(s) + 3\ H_2O(l) \rightarrow 3\ LiOH(aq) + NH_3(g)$

This would be uneconomical, as one would need to produce lithium metal first, a highly energy-intensive electrolytic process, in order to synthesize the lithium nitride:

$6\ Li(s) + N_2(g) \rightarrow 2\ Li_3N(s)$

15.65 $HONH_2$ (or NH_2OH, hydroxylamine); H_2NNO_2; $(NH_2)_2CO$ (urea).

15.67 $2\ NCl_3(g) \rightarrow N_2(g) + 3\ Cl_2(g)$

Using bond energy values from the Appendix:

Bonds broken:	6(N–Cl)	= 6(192 kJ)	= 1152 kJ
		Total	= 1152 kJ
Bonds formed:	(N≡N)		= 942 kJ
	3(Cl–Cl)	= 3(240) kJ	= 720 kJ
		Total	= 1662 kJ

Net energy change = +1152 kJ − 1662 kJ = −510 kJ

The reaction is highly exothermic due primarily to the strength of the nitrogen-nitrogen triple bond.

15.69 Only two hydrogens are replaced because the structure contains only two hydroxyl groups. The hydrogen bonded to the phosphorus is not labile and cannot be replaced.

$(HO)_2HPO_2(D_2O) + 2\ D_2O(l) \rightarrow (DO)_2HPO_2(D_2O) + 2\ HDO(D_2O)$

15.71 NO_2^+ and CNO^- are isoelectronic with the azide ion.

15.73 A very large low-charge anion – such as the hexafluoroosmate ion, $[OsF_6]^-$ ion – might stabilize the pentanitrogen cation.

15.75 (a) Silver(I) or lead(II) or mercury(I).

(b) $N_3^-(aq) + H_2O(l) \rightarrow HN_3(aq) + OH^-(aq)$

(c) The azide ion will decompose on heating to give nitrogen gas.

15.77 We can write half-reactions as if the reaction took place in solution, provided that when the final balanced equation is derived, the hydrogen ions and electrons "cancel out."

$(NH_4)[N(NO_2)_2](s) + 4\ H^+(aq) + 4\ e^- \rightarrow 4\ H_2O(g) + 2\ N_2(g)$

$2\ Al(s) + 3\ H_2O(g) \rightarrow Al_2O_3(s) + 6\ H^+(aq) + 6\ e^-$

Balanced equation:

$3\ (NH_4)[N(NO_2)_2](s) + 4\ Al(s) \rightarrow 2\ Al_2O_3(s) + 6\ H_2O(g) + 6\ N_2(g)$

Reasons for its exothermicity:

      (a) the formation of dinitrogen, with its strong triple bond;

      (b) the formation of water with strong (O–H) bonds;

      (c) the formation of aluminum oxide with the very high lattice energy

It would be a good propellant because of the large volume of gas produced per mole of ADN.

15.79   Zinc and sulfuric acid are added to the sample, which we will assume contains the arsenate ion:

$Zn(s) + H_2SO_4(aq) \rightarrow ZnSO_4(aq) + H_2(g)$

The hydrogen gas reduces the arsenate ion to arsine:

$9\ H_2(g) + 2\ AsO_4^{2-}(aq) + 4\ H^+(aq) \rightarrow 2\ AsH_3(g) + 8\ H_2O(l)$

The released arsine gas is then passed through a hot tube where it decomposes to give a metallic-looking deposit of arsenic:

$2\ AsH_3(g) \xrightarrow{\ \Delta\ } 2\ As(s) + 3\ H_2(g)$

Chapter 16

THE GROUP 16 ELEMENTS

Exercises

16.1 (a) $2\ Fe(s) + 3\ O_2(g) \rightarrow 2\ Fe_2O_3(s)$

(b) $BaS(s) + 4\ O_3(s) \rightarrow BaSO_4(s) + 4\ O_2(g)$

(c) $BaO_2(s) + 2\ H_2O(l) \rightarrow Ba(OH)_2(aq) + H_2O_2(aq)$

(d) $2\ KOH(aq) + CO_2(g) \rightarrow K_2CO_3(aq) + H_2O(l)$

$K_2CO_3(aq) + CO_2(g) + H_2O(l) \rightarrow 2\ KHCO_3(aq)$

(e) $Na_2S(aq) + H_2SO_4(aq) \rightarrow Na_2SO_4(aq) + H_2S(g)$

(f) $Na_2SO_3(aq) + H_2SO_4(aq) \rightarrow Na_2SO_4(aq) + SO_2(g) + H_2O(l)$

(g) $8\ Na_2SO_3(aq) + S_8(s) \rightarrow 8\ Na_2S_2O_3(aq)$

16.3 Polonium is the only element of the group to have an electrical resistivity low enough to be considered metallic.

16.5 (a) Finely divided metals that are spontaneously flammable in air.
(b) Different crystal forms of an element in which identical molecular units are packed differently.
(c) Unusual type of equilibria found with hemoglobin in which addition of one oxygen molecule increases the ease of addition of subsequent oxygen molecules.

16.7 Photosynthesis has resulted in the conversion to dioxygen of most of the carbon dioxide that was in the Earth's atmosphere. On Venus, there is no dioxygen, only carbon dioxide.

16.9 The bond order should be that of ozone itself—about $1\frac{1}{2}$. Using the molecular orbital approach, the electron would be removed from one of the nonbonding orbitals, so there would be no effect on bond order. From simple bonding models, we obtain the same result.

Also, by comparison with the isoelectronic nitrogen dioxide molecule, we would argue that the electron would be lost from the central oxygen's lone pair, opening out the bond angle to greater than 120°.

16.11   We would expect a larger angle for dibromine oxide compared to dichlorine oxide, both from the Bent rule and from consideration of steric crowding by the two large bromine atoms.

16.13   See the diagram. The oxidation number of +1 for oxygen is extremely rare and is a result of each atom being sandwiched between a more electronegative fluorine atom on one side and an identical atom of oxygen on the other.

$$\quad -1 \quad +1 \quad +1 \quad -1$$

16.15   Among the Group 16 elements, it is only sulfur that readily catenates. With the high stability of oxygen multiple bonds, it is extremely rare to find chains of oxygen atoms. It is probable that the high electronegativity of the end group that "pulls" electron density away from the oxygen chain and in some way stabilizes it.

16.17   The structures are:

16.19   The structure is probably based on the S_8 ring. As the NH combination has the same number of outer electrons as sulfur, it could simply replace alternate sulfur atoms around the ring and retain the same electron configuration.

16.21   The terminal oxygen atoms have "normal" oxidation states of −2, while sulfur has the common value of +6. The linked oxygen atoms are peroxide-type with oxidation states of −1.

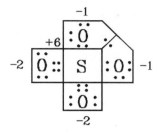

16.23   Whitewash was effective because the calcium hydroxide reacted with carbon dioxide from the air to form opaque calcium carbonate:

$$Ca(OH)_2(s) + CO_2(g) \rightarrow CaCO_3(s) + H_2O(l)$$

16.25   As the yellow solid sulfur is heated, it first melts to give a low-viscosity, straw-colored liquid. This consists of S_8 molecules. As the temperature is increased, the liquid darkens and becomes very viscous. Over this range, the S_8 rings are breaking open to form long polymer chains. At higher temperatures still, the viscosity decreases as the average chain length decreases. When the liquid boils gaseous green, S_8 molecules are produced, and at even higher temperatures, the gas turns violet as the rings break into S_2 molecules analogous to O_2.

16.27   The closeness of the bond angle in H_2Te to 90° suggests that the central tellurium atom is using pure p orbitals in its bonding.

16.29   Sulfuric acid can act as an acid (usually when dilute); as a dehydrating agent (when concentrated), as an oxidizing agent (when hot and concentrated), as a sulfonating agent (when concentrated), and as a base with stronger acids.

16.31   The most likely formal charge arrangements for sulfur trioxide and the sulfite ion are shown in (a) and (b), respectively. In the former, the average bond is $1\frac{2}{3}$, while the average bond in the latter is $1\frac{1}{3}$. Thus sulfur trioxide will have the stronger bonds (this has been established—the S–O bond length in sulfur trioxide is 142 pm while that in the sulfite ion is 151 pm).

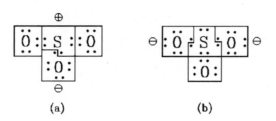

(a)   (b)

16.33   The formal charge representations are:

(a)   (b)

16.35   (a) A black precipitate of lead(II) sulfide is produced from a colorless lead(II) acetate solution:

$$H_2S(g) + Pb(CH_3COO)_2(aq) \rightarrow PbS(s) + 2\ CH_3COOH(aq)$$

(b) A white precipitate is produced when a solution of barium ion is added to sulfate ion:

$$Ba^{2+}(aq) + SO_4{}^{2-}(aq) \rightarrow BaSO_4(s)$$

16.37   Though the oxidation of sulfur dioxide to sulfur trioxide is thermodynamically spontaneous, it is kinetically very slow—or, in other words, there is a very high activation energy barrier to reaction.

16.39   The large tetramethylammonium cation will stabilize the large, low-charge ozonide ion.

16.41   The NS_2^+ ion is isoelectronic and isostructural with carbon disulfide, CS_2.

$$\left[\ddot{\underset{\displaystyle\cdot\cdot}{S}} :: \underset{\displaystyle\cdot\cdot}{N} :: \ddot{\underset{\displaystyle\cdot\cdot}{S}}\right]^+$$

16.43   We require small quantities of selenium for a healthy existence, but in larger quantities it is highly toxic.

Beyond the Basics

16.45   See the diagrams. The value of −668 kJ is much less than the −1209 kJ for sulfur hexafluoride. This difference is accounted for by the chlorine-chlorine bond being stronger than the fluorine-fluorine bond and the sulfur-chlorine bond being weaker than the sulfur-fluorine bond.

16.47   The ammonium salt will be less basic than the calcium salt because the ammonium ion is the conjugate base of a weak acid, so it reacts with water to produce a hydronium ion, partially neutralizing the hydroxide ion produced from the reaction of the glycollate ion with water to produce its conjugate acid.

$$NH_4^+(aq) + H_2O(l) \rightarrow H_3O^+(aq) + NH_3(aq)$$

16.49   Concentration in mol·cm^{-3} = $\dfrac{5 \times 10^5 \text{ molecules}}{\text{cm}^3} \times \dfrac{1\,\text{mol}}{6.02 \times 10^{23} \text{ molecules}}$

= 8×10^{-19} mol·cm^{-3} = 8×10^{-16} mol·L^{-1}

At SATP, 1 L of gas contains n = PV/RT mol of gas.

$$n = \frac{100\,kPa \times 1\,L}{8.31\,kPa \cdot L \cdot mol^{-1} \cdot K^{-1} \times 298\,K} = 0.04\,mol$$

Concentration in ppb = $\dfrac{8 \times 10^{-16}\,mol}{0.04\,mol} \times 10^9 = 2 \times 10^{-5}$ ppb

16.51   (a)   Length of side = 2(74 pm) + 2(126 pm) = 400 pm

(b)   Length of diagonal from mid-edge through center = 2(126) + 2(114 pm) = 480 pm

Thus length of side = 1/√2(480 pm) = 339 pm.

16.53   The S=O double bond is preferred according to formal charge principles (see the diagram). The molecule will be trigonal planar.

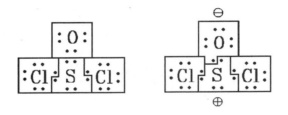

16.55   S(*s*) + O$_2$(*g*) → SO$_2$(*g*)

CaCO$_3$(*s*) + SO$_2$(*g*) → CaSO$_3$(*s*) + CO$_2$(*g*)

mol S = 1000 tonne coal × $\dfrac{3 \text{ parts S}}{100 \text{ parts coal}}$ × $\dfrac{10^6\,\text{g}}{1\,\text{tonne}}$ × $\dfrac{1 \text{ mol S}}{32.1\,\text{g}}$ = 9.3×10^5 mol S

$$\text{mass } CaCO_3 = 9.3\times10^5 \text{ mol S } \times \frac{1 \text{ mol } SO_2}{1 \text{ mol S}} \times \frac{1 \text{ mol } CaCO_3}{1 \text{ mol } SO_2} \times \frac{100.1 \text{ g}}{1 \text{ mol } CaCO_3} \times \frac{1 \text{ tonne}}{10^6 \text{ g}}$$

$$= 94 \text{ tonne}$$

16.57   Apparent oxidation number S:

$0 = 2[H] + [S] + 5[O]$

$0 = 2[+1] + [S] + 5[-2]$

$[S] = +8$, an impossible value because the oxidation number of sulfur cannot exceed 6.

$H_2SO_5 + H_2O \rightarrow H_2SO_4 + H_2O_2$ is the only equation that fits the hint. Thus a likely structure is that of sulfuric acid, $(HO)_2SO_2$, but with a peroxy- link instead of a hydroxy- link.

16.59   It is most probable that sulfite is oxidized to sulfate while peroxodisulfate is reduced to sulfate.

$SO_3^-(aq) + H_2O(l) \rightarrow SO_4^{2-}(aq) + 2 H^+(aq) + 2 e^-$

$S_2O_8^{2-}(aq) + 2 e^- \rightarrow 2 SO_4^{2-}(aq)$

$SO_3^{2-}(aq) + S_2O_8^{2-}(aq) + H_2O(l) \rightarrow 3 SO_4^{2-}(aq) + 2 H^+(aq)$

16.61 $E = E° - \dfrac{RT}{2F} \ln \dfrac{1}{[H^+]^4}$

$E = +0.17 \text{ V} - \dfrac{(8.31 \text{ C} \cdot \text{V} \cdot \text{mol}^{-1} \cdot \text{K}^{-1})(298 \text{ K})}{(2)(9.65\times10^4 \text{ C} \cdot \text{mol}^{-1})} \ln\left(\dfrac{1}{(1.0\times10^{-14})^4}\right)$

$E = +0.17 \text{ V} - 1.65 \text{ V} = -1.48 \text{ V}$

16.63   [A] Sulfur dioxide; [B] potassium hydroxide; [C] potassium sulfite; [D] sulfur; [E] thiosulfate ion; [F] tetrathionate ion; [G] thiosulfuric acid.

$SO_2(g) + 2 KOH(aq) \rightarrow K_2SO_3(aq)$

$K^+(aq) + [B(C_6H_5)_4]^-(aq) \rightarrow K[B(C_6H_5)_4](s)$

$K_2SO_3(aq) + S(s) \rightarrow K_2S_2O_3(aq)$

$$2 \ S_2O_3{}^{2-}(aq) + I_2(aq) \rightarrow S_4O_6{}^{2-}(aq) + 2 \ I^-(aq)$$

$$S_2O_3{}^{2-}(aq) + 2 \ H^+(aq) \rightarrow H_2S_2O_3(aq)$$

$$H_2S_2O_3(aq) \rightarrow H_2O(l) + S(s) + SO_2(g)$$

16.65   The triple-bond structure is more likely because there are no formal charges in the electron arrangement.

16.67   Rubidium or cesium. A large low-charge cation is necessary to stabilize the low-charge anion.

16.69   In SF_2, the sulfur has a formal oxidation state of +2. In F_3SSF, the sulfur that is surrounded by three fluorines will have the higher oxidation state of +3 (note the lone pair on this sulfur atom), while the sulfur attached to only one fluorine will have an oxidation state of +1.

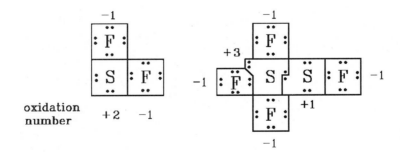

16.71. It could be a trigonal planar molecule. It could hypothetically be formed
by reaction of ozone with atomic oxygen:

$$O_3(g) + O(g) \rightarrow O_4(g)$$

The species would be isoelectronic and isostructural with the carbonate
ion and the nitrate ion (and isostructural with the gaseous monomeric
sulfur trioxide).

Chapter 17

THE GROUP 17 ELEMENTS: THE HALOGENS

Exercises

17.1 (a) $UO_2(s) + 4\ HF(g) \rightarrow UF_4(s) + 2\ H_2O(l)$

    (b) $CaF_2(s) + H_2SO_4(l) \rightarrow 2\ HF(g) + CaSO_4(s)$

    (c) $SCl_4(l) + 2\ H_2O(l) \rightarrow SO_2(g) + 4\ HCl(g)$

    (d) $3\ Cl_2(aq) + 6\ NaOH(aq) \rightarrow NaClO_3(aq) + 5\ NaCl(s) + 3\ H_2O(l)$

    (e) $I_2(s) + 5\ F_2(g) \rightarrow 2\ IF_5(s)$

    (f) $BrCl_3(l) + 2\ H_2O(l) \rightarrow 3\ HCl(aq) + HBrO_2(aq)$

17.3 Fluorine has a very weak fluorine-fluorine bond; it is usually limited to one or two covalent bonds; its compounds with metals are often ionic when those of the comparable chlorides are covalent; it has an extremely high electronegativity and forms the strongest hydrogen bonds known; it tends to stabilize high oxidation states; the solubility of its metal compounds for a particular metal is often quite different than those of the other halides.

17.5 The reaction with nonmetals is strongly enthalpy-driven because weak fluorine-fluorine bonds are broken and strong bonds are formed between fluorine and other nonmetals.

17.7 The chemical equation is
$$I_2(s) + 7\ F_2(g) \rightarrow 2\ IF_7(s)$$
Thus there is a decrease of seven moles of gas in this spontaneous reaction. Hence enthalpy decrease must be the driving force of the reaction.

17.9 The half-equation is:
$$\tfrac{1}{2}\ Cl_2(aq) + e^- \rightarrow Cl^-(aq)$$
Because hydrogen ion does not appear in the half-equation, the reduction potential will not be pH sensitive.

17.11 In the ionization of a hydrohalic acid,

$$HX(aq) + H_2O(l) \rightarrow H_3O^+(aq) + X^-(aq)$$

the H–X bond must be broken. The H–F bond is particularly strong, and as a result the equilibrium will tend to lie to the left and hydrofluoric acid will behave as a weak acid.

17.13 Chemical equation:

$$CaF_2(s) + H_2SO_4(l) \rightarrow CaSO_4(s) + 2\ HF(g)$$

Mass of hydrogen fluoride $= 1.2 \times 10^{12}$ g

Moles of hydrogen fluoride $= 6.0 \times 10^{10}$ mol

Moles of calcium sulfate $= 3.0 \times 10^{10}$ mol

Mass of calcium sulfate $= 4.1 \times 10^{12}$ g $= 4.1 \times 10^6$ tonne

17.15 Oxygen has the unusual oxidation number of zero in this compound.

$$\boxed{H \quad \ddot{\ddot{O}} \quad \ddot{\ddot{F}}:}$$
$$\quad +1 \qquad -1$$

17.17 (a) To form the higher oxidation state of a metal, dichlorine should be used:

$$2\ Cr(s) + 3\ Cl_2(g) \rightarrow 2\ CrCl_3(s)$$

(b) To form the lower oxidation state of a metal, iodine monochloride should be used:

$$Cr(s) + 2\ ICl(l) \rightarrow CrCl_2(s) + I_2(s)$$

17.19 Iron(III) iodide will not be stable because iodide ion is a reducing agent, hence it will reduce iron(III) to iron(II):

$$2\ I^- \rightarrow I_2 + 2\ e^-$$
$$Fe^{3+} + e^- \rightarrow Fe^{2+}$$

17.21 The chemical equation is

$$6\ NH_4ClO_4(s) + 8\ Al(s) \rightarrow 4\ Al_2O_3(s) + 3\ N_2(g) + 3\ Cl_2(g) + 12\ H_2O(g)$$

Thus $\Delta H = 12[\Delta H_f(H_2O(g))] + 4[\Delta H_f(Al_2O_3(s))] - 6[\Delta H_f(NH_4ClO_4(s))]$

(because the other species are elements in their standard phases)

$\Delta H \quad = 12[-242\ \text{kJ}] + 4[-1676\ \text{kJ}] - 6[+295\ \text{kJ}]$

$\qquad = -7838\ \text{kJ}$

It would also be a good propellant because it produces a large number of small gas molecules; thus it would have a high thrust per unit mass.

17.23   The half-equations for the first reaction,

$$H_2S(g) + 2\ H_2O(l) \rightarrow SO_2(g) + 6\ H^+(aq) + 6\ e^-$$

$$I_2O_5(s) + 10\ H^+(aq) + 10\ e^- \rightarrow I_2(s) + 5\ H_2O(l)$$

give an overall equation of

$$10\ H_2S(g) + 6\ I_2O_5(s) \rightarrow 10\ SO_2(g) + 6\ I_2(s) + 10\ H_2O(l)$$

For the second reaction:

$$I_2(s) + 2\ S_2O_3{}^{2-}(aq) \rightarrow 2\ I^-(aq) + S_4O_6{}^{2-}(aq)$$

17.25   Three arguments can be used: first, that the sulfur atom is too small to accomodate six iodine atoms around it; second, that iodine is reducing, thus such a high oxidation state cannot be stabilized; and third, that the sulfur-iodine bond energy is not sufficient to provide an exothermic balance to the decrease in entropy that would result from consuming six moles of gas per mole of compound formed.

17.27   The central chlorine atom has a +7 oxidation number and the end chlorine has a +1 oxidation number. Both oxidation numbers are common for chlorine.

17.29   As iodine can almost be classed as a semimetal (for example, it is known in the +1 oxidation state), we would predict astatine to start to show some metallic properties; thus the diatomic element might be a significant electrical conductor. Like the other halogens, astatine should have a common oxidation state of -1 and form an insoluble compound with silver ion:

$$Ag^+(aq) + At^-(aq) \rightarrow AgAt(s)$$

The compound should be insoluble in concentrated ammonia solution. All of the other halogens should displace its anion. For example, iodine should react as follows:

$$I_2(aq) + 2\ At^-(aq) \rightarrow 2\ I^-(aq) + At_2(s)$$

Astatine should form interhalogen compounds, such as AtF and AtI, in which astatine has a positive polarity. In fact, being so near the metal/nonmetal border, astatine will probably have a significant cation chemistry, forming, perhaps, At^+ and At^{3+}.

17.31   Structure (c), with the charge on the sulfur atom, must be the major contributor with, possibly, some small contribution from structure (a). In view of the high formal charge, contributions from structure (b) can be ignored.

formal
charge

(a)   (b)   (c)

17.33   Fluorine:

$$Cl_2(g) + 3\ F_2(g) \rightarrow 2\ ClF_3(g)$$

$$S(s) + 3\ F_2(g) \rightarrow SF_6(g)$$

$$BrO_3^-(aq) + F_2(g) + 2\ OH^-(aq) \rightarrow BrO_4^-(aq) + 2\ F^-(aq) + H_2O(l)$$

$$2\ Fe(s) + 3\ F_2(g) \rightarrow 2\ FeF_3(s)$$

$$H_2(g) + F_2(g) \rightarrow 2\ HF(g)$$

$$2\ F^-(KH_2F_3) \rightarrow F_2(g) + 2\ e^-$$

$$HF(aq) + OH^-(aq) \rightarrow H_2O(l) + F^-(aq)$$

$$HF(aq) + F^-(aq) \rightarrow HF_2^-(aq)$$

$$6\ HF(aq) + SiO_2(s) \rightarrow SiF_6^{2-}(aq) + 2\ H^+(aq) + 2\ H_2O(l)$$

$$4\ HF(g) + UO_2(s) \rightarrow UF_4(s) + 2\ H_2O(g)$$

$$UF_4(s) + F_2(g) \rightarrow UF_6(g)$$

Chlorine:

$$P_4(s) + 10\ Cl_2(g) \rightarrow 4\ PCl_5(s)$$

$$2\ Fe(s) + 3\ Cl_2(g) \rightarrow 2\ FeCl_3(s)$$

$$3\ Cl_2(g) + NH_3(g) \rightarrow NCl_3(l) + 3\ HCl(g)$$

$$Cl_2(aq) + 2\ OH^-(aq) \rightarrow Cl^-(aq) + ClO^-(aq) + H_2O(l)$$

$$ClO^-(aq) + H^+(aq) \rightarrow HClO(aq)$$

$$2\ ClO^-(aq) + Ca^{2+}(aq) \rightarrow Ca(ClO)_2(s)$$

$$Cl_2(g) + H_2(g) \rightarrow 2\ HCl(g)$$

$$2\ HCl(g) + Fe(s) \rightarrow FeCl_2(s) + H_2(g)$$

$$3\ Cl_2(aq) + 6\ OH^-(aq) \rightarrow ClO_3^-(aq) + 5\ Cl^-(aq) + 3\ H_2O(l)$$

$$ClO_3^-(aq) + H_2O(l) \rightarrow ClO_4^-(aq) + 2\ H^+(aq) + 2\ e^-$$

$$2\ ClO_3^-(aq) + 4\ H^+(aq) + 2\ Cl^-(aq) \rightarrow 2\ ClO_2(aq) + Cl_2(g) + 2\ H_2O(l)$$

Iodine:

$$I_2(s) + Cl_2(g) \rightarrow 2\ ICl(s)$$

$$I_2(s) + 2\ S_2O_3^{2-}(aq) \rightarrow 2\ I^-(aq) + S_4O_6^{2-}(aq)$$

$$2\ I^-(aq) + Cl_2(g) \rightarrow I_2(aq) + 2\ Cl^-(aq)$$

$$I^-(aq) + I_2(aq) \rightarrow I_3^-(aq)$$

17.35   Chlorine oxidation state = +1, oxygen = –1.

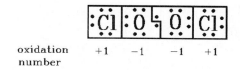

oxidation   +1   –1   –1   +1
number

17.37   The large low-charge iodide anion will stabilize the large low-charge cation.

17.39   Bromine monofluoride, BrF, would be an analog of dichlorine, Cl_2. Note that here we are using *combo* to indicate a combination of elements of the same group, but elements of period ($n–1$) and ($n+1$) as analogs of the element in period n.

17.41   (a) $(CN)_2$; (b) AgCN, or $Pb(CN)_2$, or $Hg_2(CN)_2$.

17.43 $P(CN)_3$

Beyond the Basics

17.45   The ammonium hydrogen fluoride may be decomposing and dissolving in the hydrogen fluoride produced.

$$(NH_4)^+(HF_2)^-(s) \rightarrow NH_4^+(HF) + F^-(HF)$$

17.47   The bond order will be $(3 - 2) = 1$.

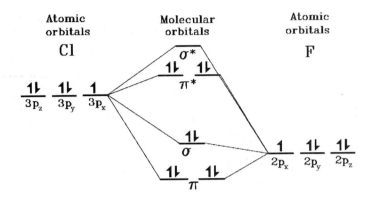

17.49   Dichlorine heptaoxide. It is the oxide in the higher oxidation state (with more oxygen atoms) that will be acidic.

17.51   Each chlorine atom will be approximately tetrahedrally coordinated, one chlorine with one lone pair and the other chlorine with two. Thus the bond angles will be approximately 109½°. Though the electron-dot structure depicts singly bonded oxygens, there is certainly multiple-bond character.

17.53 The perchlorate ion is a strong oxidizing agent, but it needs to be mixed with an oxidizable compound or element in order to have explosive properties. In ammonium perchlorate, the easily oxidizable ammonium ion is an integral part of the compound. Thus no additional component is required to cause a vigorous redox reaction.

$2 \ NH_4ClO_4(s) \rightarrow N_2(g) + Cl_2(g) + 2 \ O_2(g) + 4 \ H_2O(g)$

Nitrogen is oxidized from −3 to 0, chlorine is reduced from +7 to 0, and oxygen is oxidized from −2 to 0.

17.55 The structures follow. Single Cl–O bonds would be equally acceptable.

17.57 $Tl^+(I_3)^-$. Iodide is a reducing agent and it would be expected to reduce thallium(III) to thallium(I).

17.59   (a)   The azide (N_3^-) ion, acts as a pseudohalide ion. Thus it can form a pseudo-interhalide ion by substituting for two of the iodine atoms in I_3^-, thus $[I(N_3)_2]^-$.

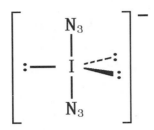

(b)   The azide must be of higher electronegativity than iodide because it is the less electronegative element that is the center of a cluster.

(c)   The iodide ion has seven electrons plus one from the negative charge. It will "share" one with each of the azide units, giving a total of ten electrons, or five electron pairs. Hence there will be a trigonal bipyramid electron-pair arrangement. Because the three lone pairs will occupy equatorial positions, the molecular shape will be linear.

(d)   The ion would be stabilized in the solid phase by a large cation such as rubidium or cesium.

17.61   (a) $ClF_3(l) + BF_3(g) \rightarrow ClF_2^+(ClF_3) + BF_4^-(ClF_3)$

(b) $ClF_3(l) + KF(s) \rightarrow K^+(ClF_3) + ClF_4^-(ClF_3)$

(c)   In (a), the B–F bond is much stronger (613 kJ·mol^{-1}) than the Cl–F bond (249 kJ·mol^{-1}), so the boron can abstract a fluorine from the chlorine. In (b), the Cl–F bond strength must be greater than the energy needed to extract a fluoride ion from the potassium fluoride lattice.

Chapter 18

THE GROUP 18 ELEMENTS: THE NOBLE GASES

Exercises

18.1   (a) $Xe(g) + 2 F_2(g) \rightarrow XeF_4(s)$

(b) $XeF_4(s) + 2 PF_3(g) \rightarrow 2 PF_5(g) + Xe(g)$

18.3   Descending the group, the melting and boiling points increase, as do the densities.

18.5   Helium cannot be solidified at any temperature under normal pressure; when cooled close to absolute zero, liquid helium (helium II) becomes an incredible thermal conductor and its viscosity drops to close to zero.

18.7   Assuming the molecular orbitals formed from $5p$ atomic orbitals are similar to those formed from $2p$ atomic orbitals, we can construct the following diagram and deduce that the bond order must be ½.

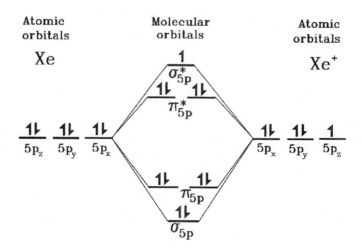

18.9   The thermodynamic factors are the weakness of the fluorine-fluorine bond that has to be broken in the energy cycle and the comparative strength of the xenon-fluorine bond that is formed.

18.11

18.13   The double-bond structure has zero formal charge while the single-bond representation has a negative charge on the oxygen and a positive charge on the xenon. Thus the double-bonded structure probably makes a major contribution to the bonding.

18.15   Using the calculation method:

(a) $[N_{ox}(Xe)] + 3(-1) = +1$
$[N_{ox}(Xe)] = +4$

(b) $[N_{ox}(Xe)] + 5(-1) = +1$
$[N_{ox}(Xe)] = +6$

(c) $[N_{ox}(Xe)] + 6(-2) = -4$
$[N_{ox}(Xe)] = +8$

18.17   Rubidium or cesium, because a large low-charge cation is needed to stabilize a large low-charge anion.

18.19   Half reactions:

$Au \rightarrow Au^{5+} + 5\ e^-$

$KrF_2 + 2\ e^- \rightarrow Kr + 2\ F^-$

Redox reaction:

$2\ Au + 5\ KrF_2 \rightarrow 2\ AuF_5 + 5\ Kr$

Plus two extra KrF_2 to result in salt formation:

$2\ Au + 7\ KrF_2 \rightarrow 2\ (KrF)^+(AuF_6^-) + 5\ Kr$

18.21 $Xe(g) + F_2(g) \rightarrow XeF_2(s)$

$2\ XeF_2(s) + 2\ H_2O(l) \rightarrow 2\ Xe(g) + O_2(g) + 4\ HF(l)$

$Xe(g) + 2\ F_2(g) \rightarrow XeF_4(s)$

$Xe(g) + 3\ F_2(g) \rightarrow XeF_6(s)$

$XeF_6(s) + H_2O(l) \rightarrow XeOF_4(l) + 2\ HF(l)$

$XeOF_4(l) + 2\ H_2O(l) \rightarrow XeO_3(s) + 4\ HF(l)$

$XeO_3(s) + OH^-(aq) \rightarrow HXeO_4^-(aq)$

$2\ HXeO_4^-(aq) + 2\ OH^-(aq) \rightarrow XeO_6^{4-}(aq) + Xe(g) + O_2(g) + H_2O(l)$

$XeO_6^{4-}(aq) + 2\ Ba^{2+}(aq) \rightarrow Ba_2XeO_6(s)$

$Ba_2XeO_6(s) + 2\ H_2SO_4(aq) \rightarrow 2\ BaSO_4(s) + XeO_4(g) + 2\ H_2O(l)$

Beyond the Basics

18.23 $XeF_2(SbF_5) + SbF_5(l) \rightarrow XeF^+(SbF_5) + SbF_6^-(SbF_5)$

18.25 $Ar(g) + F_2(g) \rightarrow ArF_2(g)$

Even assuming argon difluoride would be a gas, there is a decrease in entropy in the synthesis. Thus the enthalpy change has to be less than zero (exothermic). Assuming zero is the limiting value, we can construct an energy cycle. Thus the Ar–F bond energy can be no more than 77.5 $kJ \cdot mol^{-1}$.

Chapter 19

INTRODUCTION TO TRANSITION METAL COMPLEXES

Exercises

19.1   (a) Element belonging to the *d*-block, though usually Groups 3 and 12 are excluded.

(b) Molecules or ions covalently bonded to a central metal ion.

(c) Energy separation between different members of the metal's *d*-orbital set when the metal ion is surrounded by a set of ligands.

19.3   The cyanide ligand stabilizes low oxidation states (in a similar manner to carbon monoxide) and also stabilizes normal oxidation states (as a pseudohalide ion).

19.5 $[Pt(NH_3)_4]^{2+}[PtCl_4]^{2-}$

19.7   The geometric isomers are:

And for one of the geometric isomers, there are two optical (chiral) isomers.

19.9   (a) Ammonium pentachlorocuprate(II); (b) pentaammineaquacobalt(III) bromide; (c) potassium tetracarbonylchromate(-III); (d) potassium hexafluoronickelate(IV); (e) tetraamminecopper(II) perchlorate.

19.11   (a) $[Mn(OH_2)_6](NO_3)_2$.
        (b) $Pd[PdF_6]$.
        (c) $[CrCl_2(OH_2)_4]Cl\cdot 2\,H_2O$.
        (d) $K_3[Mo(CN)_8]$.

19.13   (a) The d^6 configuration in an octahedral field:

19.13   (b) The d^6 configuration in a tetrahedral field:

19.15   The largest value of Δ is for the cobalt(III) complex, the others being cobalt(II) because the splitting increases with increase in oxidation state. The smallest value is for cobalt(II) in a tetrahedral environment compared to the middle cobalt(II) in an octahedral environment because Δ_{tet} is only about four-ninths the value of Δ_{oct}.

19.17 (a) $[ReF_6]^{2-}$, because the heavier metal will have the greater crystal field splitting.

(b) $[Fe(CN)_6]^{3-}$, because the higher charge Fe(III) will have the greater crystal field splitting.

19.19 Configuration   CFSE

Configuration	CFSE
d^0	$-0.0\ \Delta_{tet}$
d^1	$-0.6\ \Delta_{tet}$
d^2	$-1.2\ \Delta_{tet}$
d^3	$-0.8\ \Delta_{tet}$
d^4	$-0.4\ \Delta_{tet}$
d^5	$-0.0\ \Delta_{tet}$
d^6	$-0.6\ \Delta_{tet}$
d^7	$-1.2\ \Delta_{tet}$
d^8	$-0.8\ \Delta_{tet}$
d^9	$-0.4\ \Delta_{tet}$
d^{10}	$-0.0\ \Delta_{tet}$

19.21 The optimum situation energetically is for the ion with the greater CFSE to occupy the octahedral sites. Thus the mixed metal oxide $NiCr_2O_4$ will adopt the normal spinel structure, $(Ni^{2+})_t(Cr^{3+})_oO_4$, because the Cr^{3+} ion, having the higher oxidation state, will have a greater CFSE than that of the Ni^{2+} ion.

19.23 Balanced chemical equation:

$$[Ni(OH_2)_6]^{2+}(aq) + 2\ det(aq) \rightarrow [Ni(det)_2]^{2+}(aq) + 6\ H_2O(l)$$

The formation of this product will be favored as a result of the chelate effect—the increase in entropy from the increase in moles.

Beyond the Basics

19.25 The ligand tricyclohexylphosphine is probably too large for two of them to fit around an iron(III) in addition to the three chloro-ligands.

19.27 (a) M^{2+} should disproportionate as the sum of the potentials (0.00 + 0.20) V is positive. The equation would be

$$3\ M^{2+}(aq) \rightarrow M(s) + 2\ M^{3+}(aq)$$

(b) $2 M^{2+}(aq) + 2 H^+(aq) + 2 e^- \rightarrow 2 M^{3+}(aq) + H_2(g)$

To find the limit of spontaneity, we can set E = 0.

Because only the hydrogen-ion concentration varies, we can write a simplified Nernst equation:

$$E = 0 = E° - \frac{RT}{2F}\ln\left(\frac{1}{[H^+]^2}\right) = +0.20\ V - \frac{8.31\ V\cdot C\cdot mol^{-1}\cdot K^{-1}\times 298\ K}{2\times(9.65\times 10^4\ C\cdot mol^{-1})}\ln\left(\frac{1}{[H^+]^2}\right)$$

$[H^+] = 4.1\times 10^{-4}$

pH = 3.38

19.29   For zinc, with its filled d^{10} orbitals, there is no crystal field stabilization energy; thus geometry is primarily determined by electron-pair repulsions. For nickel, a square-planar geometry will maximize CFSE and it will enable some degree of π bonding to occur between the part-empty d orbitals of the nickel and the filled d orbitals of the selenium.

19.31   (a) $[Cr(OH_2)_6]^{3+}\cdot 3Cl^-$, hexaaquachromium(III) chloride;
         (b) $[Cr(OH_2)_5Cl]^{2+}\cdot 2Cl^-$, pentaaquachlorochromium(III) chloride;
         (c) $[Cr(OH_2)_4Cl_2]^+\cdot Cl^-$, tetraaquadichlorochromium(III) chloride.

19.33   Fluoride is a weaker field ligand than chloride. Thus the crystal-field splitting for the fluoro- compound will be less than that of the chloro- compound. To give a yellow-orange color, the chloro- compound must be absorbing in the blue (higher energy) portion of the spectrum. To give a blue color, the fluoro- compound must be absorbing in the red (lower energy) portion of the spectrum.

Chapter 20

PROPERTIES OF THE 3d TRANSITION METALS

Exercises

20.1　(a)　$TiCl_4(l) + O_2(g) \rightarrow TiO_2(s) + 2\ Cl_2(g)$

　　　(b)　$Na_2Cr_2O_7(s) + S(l) \rightarrow Cr_2O_3(s) + Na_2SO_4(s)$

　　　(c)　$Cu(OH)_2(s) \rightarrow CuO(s) + H_2O(l)$

20.3　For the earlier part of the Period 4 transition metals, the maximum oxidation number is the same as the group number (that is, the sum of the $4s$ and $3d$ electrons). For the later members, the oxidation state of +2 predominates.

20.5　Titanium(IV) chloride vaporizes readily, a characteristic of a covalent compound. Covalent behavior would be expected on the basis of the high charge density of the Ti^{4+} ion resulting in a strong attraction for the large, low charge density chloride ions (that is, covalent bond formation).

20.7　(a)　$MnO_4^-(aq) + 8\ H^+(aq) + 5\ e^- \rightarrow Mn^{2+}(aq) + 4\ H_2O(l)$

　　　(b)　$MnO_4^-(aq) + 2\ H_2O(l) + 3\ e^- \rightarrow MnO_2(s) + 4\ OH^-(aq)$

20.9　Iron(II) chloride is prepared under comparatively reducing conditions as a result of the hydrogen gas production:

　　　　$Fe(s) + 2\ HCl(g) \rightarrow FeCl_2(s) + H_2(g)$

　　Iron(III) chloride is prepared using highly oxidizing chlorine gas:

　　　　$2\ Fe(s) + 3\ Cl_2(g) \rightarrow 2\ FeCl_3(s)$

20.11 (a) Cobalt:

$$[Co(OH_2)_6]^{2+}(aq) + 4\ Cl^-(aq) \rightarrow [CoCl_4]^{2-}(aq) + 6\ H_2O(l)$$

(b) Copper:

$$2\ Cu(s) + 2\ H^+(aq) + 4\ Cl^-(aq) \rightarrow 2\ [CuCl_2]^-(aq) + H_2(g)$$

$$[CuCl_2]^-(aq) \rightarrow CuCl(s) + Cl^-(aq)$$

(c) Chromium:

$$2\ CrO_4{}^{2-}(aq) + 2\ H^+(aq) \rightarrow Cr_2O_7{}^{2-}(aq) + H_2O(l)$$

20.13 The two reactants are the hexaaquairon(III) ion and thiosulfate ion:

$$Fe^{3+}(aq) + 2\ S_2O_3{}^{2-}(aq) \rightarrow [Fe(S_2O_3)_2]^-(aq)$$

$$[Fe(S_2O_3)_2]^-(aq) + Fe^{3+}(aq) \rightarrow 2\ Fe^{2+}(aq) + S_4O_6{}^{2-}(aq)$$

20.15 (a) Fluoride stabilizes high oxidation states since it is a π-donor ligand. To maximize π interaction, the metal ion should have empty d orbitals and hence be in the highest possible oxidation state.
(b) The value of the crystal-field splitting, Δ, is very dependent upon oxidation state, so the nickel(IV) complex should have a very large Δ value. Thus, even though fluoride is very low in the spectrochemical series, the complex is most likely to be low spin.

20.17 $FeO_4{}^{2-}(aq) + 8\ H^+(aq) + 3\ e^- \rightarrow Fe^{3+}(aq) + 4\ H_2O(l)$

$2\ NH_3(aq) \rightarrow N_2(g) + 6\ H^+(aq) + 6\ e^-$

$2\ FeO_4{}^{2-}(aq) + 2\ NH_3(aq) + 10\ H^+(aq) \rightarrow 2\ Fe^{3+}(aq) + N_2(g) + 8\ H_2O(l)$

20.19 Chromium(VI) oxide. The very high charge density of the chromium metal ion will cause sufficient polarization of the electrons on the oxygens to result in covalent bond formation. Covalently bonded compounds have much lower melting points than ionic compounds (usually!).

20.21 Like aluminum and iron(III) ions, the chromium(III) ion will lose a hydrogen ion to a water molecule.

$$[Cr(OH_2)_6]^{3+}(aq) + H_2O(l) \rightarrow [Cr(OH)(OH_2)_5]^{2+}(aq) + H_3O^+(aq)$$

20.23 The insolubility of copper(I) chloride can be argued for reasons similar to those arguing why silver chloride is insoluble (Chapter 5). According to Fajan's Rules, cations with non-noble-gas configurations are likely to have a more covalent character (in this case, the filled $3d$ orbitals can be polarized towards the anions). If the ionic charge in the crystal lattice is decreased by partial electron sharing, then the ion-water interaction will be less and the tendency to dissolve will, in turn, be less.

20.25 (a) In a well-aerated lake, the partial pressure of dioxygen would lead to a high positive potential, while the pH should be near neutral. FeO(OH) is the most likely species.

(b) In acid oxidizing conditions, Fe^{3+} is the most probable species.

(c) Fe^{2+} is most likely in these acid, reducing conditions.

20.27 They both form anhydrous chlorides that react with water to release hydrogen chloride gas while their hexahydrates are water soluble. The anhydrous chlorides both function as Friedel-Craft catalysts. In the gas phase, their chlorides exist as dimers, Al_2Cl_6 and Fe_2Cl_6, respectively. On the other hand, iron(III) oxide is basic, while the oxide of aluminum is amphoteric. Also, iron(III) compounds are colored, while those of aluminum are white.

20.29 Titanium:

$$TiO_2(s) + 2\ C(s) + 2\ Cl_2(g) \xrightarrow{\Delta} TiCl_4(g) + 2\ CO(g)$$

$$TiCl_4(g) + O_2(g) \xrightarrow{\Delta} TiO_2(s) + 2\ Cl_2(g)$$

$$TiCl_4(g) + 2\ Mg(l) \xrightarrow{\Delta} Ti(s) + 2\ MgCl_2(l)$$

Vanadium:

$$[H_2VO_4]^-(aq) + 4\ H^+(aq) + e^- \rightarrow VO^{2+}(aq) + 3\ H_2O(l)$$

$$VO^{2+}(aq) + 2\ H^+(aq) + e^- \rightarrow V^{3+}(aq) + H_2O(l)$$

$$[V(OH_2)_6]^{3+}(aq) + e^- \rightarrow [V(OH_2)_6]^{2+}(aq)$$

Chromium:

$$CrO_4^{2-}(aq) + 2\ Ag^+(aq) \rightarrow Ag_2CrO_4(s)$$

$$CrO_4^{2-}(aq) + H_2O(l) \leftrightarrow HCrO_4^-(aq) + OH^-(aq)$$

$$2\ CrO_4^{2-}(aq) + 2\ H^+(aq) \rightarrow Cr_2O_7^{2-}(aq) + H_2O(l)$$

$$Cr_2O_7^{2-}(aq) + 2\ NH_4^+(aq) \rightarrow (NH_4)_2Cr_2O_7(s)$$

$$(NH_4)_2Cr_2O_7(s) \rightarrow Cr_2O_3(s) + N_2(g) + 4\ H_2O(l)$$

$$Cr_2O_7^{2-}(aq) + 14\ H^+(aq) + 6\ e^- \rightarrow 2\ Cr^{3+}(aq) + 7\ H_2O(l)$$

$Cr_2O_7^{2-}(aq) + 2\ K^+(aq) \rightarrow K_2Cr_2O_7(s)$

$K_2Cr_2O_7(s) + H_2SO_4(aq) \rightarrow 2\ CrO_3(s) + K_2SO_4(aq) + H_2O(l)$

$K_2Cr_2O_7(s) + 4\ NaCl(s) + 6\ H_2SO_4(l) \rightarrow 2\ CrO_2Cl_2(l) + 2\ KHSO_4(s)$
$$+ NaHSO_4(s) + 3\ H_2O(l)$$

$CrO_2Cl_2(l) + 4\ OH^-(aq) \rightarrow CrO_4^{2-}(aq) + 2\ Cl^-(aq) + 2\ H_2O(l)$

$Cr_2O_7^{2-}(aq) + 14\ H^+(aq) + 6\ e^- \rightarrow 2\ Cr^{3+}(aq) + 7\ H_2O(l)$

$2\ Cr^{3+}(aq) + Zn(s) \rightarrow 2\ Cr^{2+}(aq) + Zn^{2+}(aq)$

$2\ Cr^{2+}(aq) + 4\ CH_3COO^-(aq) + 2\ H_2O(l) \rightarrow Cr_2(CH_3COO)_4(OH_2)_2(s)$

Manganese:

$MnO_4^-(aq) + e^- \rightarrow MnO_4^{2-}(aq)$

$MnO_4^{2-}(aq) + 2\ H_2O(l) + 2\ e^- \rightarrow MnO_2(s) + 4\ OH^-(aq)$

$MnO_4^-(aq) + 2\ H_2O(l) + 3\ e^- \rightarrow MnO_2(s) + 4\ OH^-(aq)$

$MnO_4^-(aq) + 8\ H^+(aq) + 5\ e^- \rightarrow Mn^{2+}(aq) + 4\ H_2O(l)$

$Mn^{2+}(aq) + 2\ OH^-(aq) \rightarrow Mn(OH)_2(s)$

$Mn(OH)_2(s) + OH^-(aq) \rightarrow MnO(OH)(s) + H_2O(l) + e^-$

Iron:

$[Fe(OH_2)_6]^{3+}(aq) + SCN^-(aq) \rightarrow [Fe(SCN)(OH_2)_5]^{2+}(aq) + H_2O(l)$

$[Fe(OH_2)_6]^{3+}(aq) + 4\ Cl^-(aq) \leftrightarrow [FeCl_4]^-(aq) + 6\ H_2O(l)$

$Fe^{3+}(aq) + 3\ OH^-(aq) \rightarrow FeO(OH)(s) + H_2O(l)$

$[Fe(OH_2)_6]^{3+}(aq) + e^- \rightarrow [Fe(OH_2)_6]^{2+}(aq)$

$Fe^{3+}(aq) + 2\ S_2O_3^{2-}(aq) \rightarrow [Fe(S_2O_3)_2]^-(aq)$

$[Fe(S_2O_3)_2]^-(aq) + Fe^{3+}(aq) \rightarrow 2\ Fe^{2+}(aq) + S_4O_6^{2-}(aq)$

$Fe^{2+}(aq) + 2\ OH^-(aq) \rightarrow Fe(OH)_2(s)$

$[Fe(OH_2)_6]^{2+}(aq) + NO(aq) \rightarrow [Fe(NO)(OH_2)_5]^{2+}(aq) + H_2O(l)$

$Fe(OH)_2(s) + OH^-(aq) \rightarrow FeO(OH)(s) + H_2O(l) + e^-$

$Fe^{2+}(aq) + 2\ e^- \rightarrow Fe(s)$

$2\ Fe(s) + 3\ Cl_2(g) \rightarrow 2\ FeCl_3(s)$

$Fe(s) + 2\ HCl(g) \rightarrow FeCl_2(s) + H_2(g)$

Cobalt:

$[Co(OH_2)_6]^{3+}(aq) + e^- \rightarrow [Co(OH_2)_6]^{2+}(aq)$

$[Co(OH_2)_6]^{2+}(aq) + 4\ Cl^-(aq) \rightarrow [CoCl_4]^{2-}(aq) + 6\ H_2O(l)$

$Co^{2+}(aq) + 2\ OH^-(aq) \rightarrow Co(OH)_2(s)$

$Co(OH)_2(s) + 2\ OH^-(aq) \rightarrow Co(OH)_4^{2-}(aq)$

$Co(OH)_2(s) + OH^-(aq) \rightarrow CoO(OH)(s) + H_2O(l) + e^-$

$[Co(OH_2)_6]^{2+}(aq) + 6\ NH_3(aq) \rightarrow [Co(NH_3)_6]^{2+}(aq) + 6\ H_2O(l)$

$[Co(NH_3)_6]^{2+}(aq) \rightarrow [Co(NH_3)_6]^{3+}(aq) + e^-$

$O_2(g) + 2\ H_2O(l) + 4\ e^- \rightarrow 4\ OH^-(aq)$

Nickel:

$Ni(CO)_4(g) \rightarrow Ni(s) + 4\ CO(g)$

$Ni(s) \rightarrow Ni^{2+}(aq) + 2\ e^-$

$[Ni(OH_2)_6]^{2+}(aq) + 4\ Cl^-(aq) \rightarrow [NiCl_4]^{2-}(aq) + 6\ H_2O(l)$

$Ni^{2+}(aq) + 2\ OH^-(aq) \rightarrow Ni(OH)_2(s)$

$[Ni(OH_2)_6]^{2+}(aq) + 6\ NH_3(aq) \rightarrow [Ni(NH_3)_6]^{2+}(aq) + 6\ H_2O(l)$

Copper:

$2\ Cu(s) + 2\ H^+(aq) + 4\ Cl^-(aq) \rightarrow 2\ [CuCl_2]^-(aq) + H_2(g)$

$Cu^{2+}(aq) + Zn(s) \rightarrow Cu(s) + Zn^{2+}(aq)$

$Cu(s) \rightarrow Cu^{2+}(aq) + 2\ e^-$

$[Cu(OH_2)_6]^{2+}(aq) + 4\ NH_3(aq) \rightarrow [Cu(NH_3)_4]^{2+}(aq) + 6\ H_2O(l)$

$[Cu(OH_2)_6]^{2+}(aq) + 4\ Cl^-(aq) \rightarrow [CuCl_4]^{2-}(aq) + 6\ H_2O(l)$

$Cu^{2+}(aq) + 2\ OH^-(aq) \rightarrow Cu(OH)_2(s)$

$Cu(OH)_2(s) + 2\ OH^-(aq) \rightarrow [Cu(OH)_4]^{2-}(aq)$

$Cu(OH)_2(s) \rightarrow CuO(s) + H_2O(l)$

Beyond the Basics

20.31   Addition of an anhydrous calcium compound will result in formation of the hexaaquacalcium ion. This will reduce the available mole of 'free' water and hence 'drive the reaction to the right':

$$CaX_2(s) + aq \rightarrow [Ca(OH_2)_6]^{2+}(aq) + 2\ X^-(aq)$$

Addition of an anhydrous zinc compound results in the formation of the competing complexation of the zinc ion to give the tetrachlorozincate ion and hence 'drive the reaction to the left':

$$ZnX_2(s) + aq + 4\ Cl^-(aq) \rightarrow [ZnCl_4]^{2-}(aq) + 2\ X^-(aq)$$

20.33   Dichromate is in equilibrium with the chromate ion:

$Cr_2O_7^{2-}(aq) + H_2O(l) \rightarrow 2\ CrO_4^{2-}(aq) + 2\ H^+(aq)$

The chromate then reacts with the lead ion to form insoluble lead(II) chromate (the dichromate being more soluble). As chromate ion is precipitated, more is produced, according to Le Châtelier's principle.

$$Pb^{2+}(aq) + CrO_4^{2-}(aq) \rightarrow PbCrO_4(s)$$

20.35 (a)   A solution of cyanide ion will be basic:

$$CN^-(aq) + H_2O(l) \rightarrow HCN(aq) + OH^-(aq)$$

Thus the precipitate will probably be nickel(II) hydroxide:

$$Ni^{2+}(aq) + 2\ OH^-(aq) \rightarrow Ni(OH)_2(s)$$

It is unlikely to be nickel(II) cyanide. Because nickel(II) chloride is soluble, nickel(II) cyanide also should be soluble (pseudohalide ion).

(b)   This should be the square planar tetracyanonickelate(II) ion:

$$Ni(OH)_2(s) + 4\ CN^-(aq) \rightarrow [Ni(CN)_4]^{2-}(aq) + OH^-(aq)$$

(c)   This must involve the addition of a fifth cyanide ion:

$$[Ni(CN)_4]^{2-}(aq) + CN^-(aq) \rightarrow Ni(CN)_5]^{3-}(aq)$$

20.37 (a)   The high-charge cation (Fe^{3+}) will have a lowish lattice energy when combined with a low-charge anion (ClO_4^-). Solubility depends upon the competing factors of lattice energy and ion hydration enthalpies. The lowish lattice energy results in solubility. The high-charge cation (Fe^{3+}) will have a very high lattice energy when combined with a high-charge anion (PO_4^{3-}). This will be greater than the sum of the hydration enthalpies and the compound will be insoluble.

(b)   Either: Ammonia and water are quite high in the spectrochemical series whereas phosphine and hydrogen sulfide are very low.
Or: Ammonia and water are hard bases, and the first row transition metals are mostly hard acids, while phosphine and hydrogen sulfide are soft bases.

(c)   As Fe^{3+} high spin has one electron in each orbital, there is no strong color from *d-d* transitions. The color must result from charge transfer. Bromide is more easily reduced than chloride; thus the transition

$$Fe^{3+}Br^- \rightarrow Fe^{2+}Br^0$$

takes place at a lower energy (more in the visible region) than in the chloride compound.

20.39   Like the equivalent iron compound, this is probably nickel(II) disulfide(2–)—the disulfide ion being analogous to the dioxide(2–) ion. The sulfur oxidation state would be −1.

20.41   [A] Nickel(II) sulfide; [B] hydrogen sulfide; [C] hexaaquanickel(II) ion; [D] sulfur dioxide; [E] sulfur; [F] and [G] disulfur dichloride and sulfur dichloride; [H] hexaamminenickel(II) ion; [I] nickel(II) hydroxide; [J] nickel metal; [K] tetracarbonylnickel(0).

$NiS(s) + 2\ H^+(aq) \rightarrow Ni^{2+}(aq) + H_2S(g)$

$2\ H_2S(g) + 3\ O_2(g) \rightarrow 2\ H_2O(l) + 2\ SO_2(g)$

$2\ H_2S(g) + SO_2(g) \rightarrow 2\ H_2O(l) + 3\ S(s)$

$2\ S(s) + Cl_2(g) \rightarrow S_2Cl_2(l)$

$S(s) + Cl_2(g) \rightarrow SCl_2(l)$

$[Ni(OH_2)_6]^{2+}(aq) + 6\ NH_3(aq) \rightarrow [Ni(NH_3)_6]^{2+}(aq) + 6\ H_2O(l)$

$Ni^{2+}(aq) + 2\ OH^-(aq) \rightarrow Ni(OH)_2(s)$

$Ni^{2+}(aq) + Zn(s) \rightarrow Ni(s) + Zn^{2+}(aq)$

$Ni(s) + 4\ CO(g) \rightarrow Ni(CO)_4(l)$

20.43   Vanadium is the only transition metal whose chemistry matches the information provided.

20.45   Chromium-52 has 28 neutrons corresponding to a full neutron shell.

20.47   3+, as the shared oxygen would have an oxidation state of −2 (−1 with each chromium). The linear shape suggests there is a π-bonding Cr–O–Cr system. This would use the filled p orbitals on oxygen together with the part-empty d_{xy}, d_{xz}, and d_{yz} orbitals. The equivalent cobalt compound would probably have a bent Co–O–Co bond, as those d orbitals on cobalt are fully occupied and thus cannot be used for π bonding.

20.49   Under normal conditions, the reduction would be:

$$[Fe(OH_2)_6]^{3+}(aq) + e^- \rightarrow [Fe(OH_2)_6]^{2+}(aq)$$

In the presence of high concentrations of chloride ion, the reaction would become:

$$[FeCl_4]^-(aq) + e^- \rightarrow [FeCl_4]^{2-}(aq)$$

Presumably the chloride ligand has preferentially stabilized the 3+ oxidation state of the iron.

20.51   The charge transfer process can be represented as

$$Ag^+X^- \rightarrow Ag^0X^0$$

where X represents the halide ion. As the halide ion is more readily oxidized, the absorption of light will be of lower energy—more and more in the visible part of the spectrum. As iodide is the easiest oxidized and chloride the least, this represents the order of visible color intensity.

20.53   As calcium ion always has an oxidation state of 2+, it will replace the Mn^{2+} to give: $3Mn_2O_3 \cdot CaSiO_3$. Iron would most likely be in the Fe^{3+} oxidation state, in which case it would replace the Mn^{3+} ion to give: $3Fe_2O_3 \cdot MnSiO_3$. Titanium (as titanate) would replace the silicon in the silicate: $3Mn_2O_3 \cdot MnTiO_3$. Aluminum as Al^{3+} could replace the Mn^{3+} to give: $3Al_2O_3 \cdot MnSiO_3$, or as aluminate, it could replace silicon in silicate, though then the manganese would have to be Mn^{3+} to retain charge balance: $3Mn_2O_3 \cdot MnAlO_3$.

20.55   The ring structure suggests that there could be some form of π-bonding of the multiple-bonded ligands through the d orbitals of the nickel ion.

20.57   (a) $Fe(s) + O_2(g) \rightarrow Fe_2O_3(s)$

(b)   The layer of unreactive sodium silicate will coat the iron and prevent the continuation of the oxidation.

(c)   The red-hot iron would have reacted with water to give hydrogen gas.

$$2\ Fe(s) + 3\ H_2O(l) \xrightarrow{\Delta} Fe_2O_3(s) + 3\ H_2(g)$$

The explosion would have resulted from the hydrogen/oxygen mixture:

$$2\ H_2(g) + O_2(g) \rightarrow 2\ H_2O(g)$$

Chapter 21

PROPERTIES OF THE 4d AND 5d TRANSITION METALS

Exercises

21.1 (a) $2 [Ag(CN)_2]^-(aq) + Zn(s) \rightarrow 2\ Ag(s) + [Zn(CN)_4]^{2-}(aq)$

    (b) $2\ Au(s) + 3\ Cl_2(g) \rightarrow 2\ AuCl_3(s)$

21.3 For the earlier part of the 4d-5d transition metals, the maximum oxidation number is the same as the group number (that is, the sum of the 4s and 3d electrons). Discussing the 5d fluorides (see Table 17.6) the oxidation number seems to 'plateau' at seven. For example, osmium forms OsF_7, even though with oxygen, osmium can have an oxidation state of eight. It can be argued that it is impossible to fit more than seven fluorine atoms around a 5d metal ion, thus limiting the oxidation state to 7+.

21.5 (a) automobile engine lubricant; (b) antibacterial.

21.7 Osmium(VIII) oxide has a melting point of 40°C, in the range typical of covalent compounds and far below that expected for ionic compounds. In addition it is very soluble in low-polarity organic solvents – for example, OsO_4 is 500 times more soluble in tetrachloromethane than in water.

21.9 Ruthenium, rhodium, palladium, osmium, iridium, and platinum.

21.11 The 3d transition metals tend to have lower oxidation states than those of the 4d and 5d series. It is oxide rather than fluoride that 'brings out' the highest oxidation state, for example, manganese has a 7+ oxidation state in the permanganate ion, MnO_4^-. The smaller 3d ions cannot accommodate as many ligands surrounding them as the larger 4d and 5d metal ions.

21.13 For palladium, +2 and +3 are common while +2, +4, and +6 are common for platinum. Square planar is common for the lower oxidation states and octahedral geometry for the +6 state of platinum.

21.15   A quadruple bond can be formed as follows:

End-on overlap of a pair of d_{x^2} orbitals to give a σ bond;

diagonal overlap of a pair of d_{xz} orbitals to give one π bond and the overlap of a pair of d_{yz} orbitals to give the other π bond; and the side-to-side overlap of a pair of d_{xy} orbitals to give one δ bond.

21.17 PdF_3 does not contain palladium in the +3 oxidation state. Instead, it has the formulation of: $(Pd^{2+})[PdF_6]^{2-}$.

Beyond the Basics

21.19 $Au^+(aq) + e^- \rightarrow Au(s)$ $E° = +1.68$ V

$Au(s) + 2\ CN^-(aq) \rightarrow Au(CN)_2^-(aq)$ $E° = +0.60$ V

$Au^+(aq) + 2\ CN^-(aq) \rightarrow Au(CN)_2^-(aq)$ $E° = +2.28$ V

$\Delta G° = -nFE° = -RT\ln K$

$$\ln K = \frac{nFE°}{RT} = \frac{1 \times (9.65 \times 10^4\ C \cdot mol^{-1}) \times (+2.28\ V)}{8.31\ V \cdot C \cdot mol^{-1} \cdot K^{-1} \times 298\ K} = 88.8$$

$K = 3.7 \times 10^{38}$

21.21   The oxidation state is +7. This is expected because rhenium, like manganese, exhibits oxidation states as high as +7. No; hydride being a strong reducing agent, it should stabilize only low oxidation states.

21.23   No, because in all its "normal' compounds, it has a +1 oxidation state, which corresponds to a d^{10} electron configuration. The ion resembles thallium(I) most closely in terms of compound solubility—soluble fluoride but all other halides insoluble.

21.25   +5, the expected common oxidation state of niobium.

21.27   It is only the terminal bromide ions that are replaced, not the bridging atoms. The azide ion is acting as a pseudo-halide ion.

Chapter 22

THE GROUP 12 ELEMENTS

Exercises

22.1   (a) $Zn(s) + Br_2(l) \rightarrow ZnBr_2(s)$

         (b) $ZnCO_3(s) \rightarrow ZnO(s) + CO_2(g)$

22.3   React zinc metal with a dilute acid, such as hydrochloric acid, then add a soluble carbonate, such as sodium carbonate:

$$Zn(s) + 2\ H^+(aq) \rightarrow Zn^{2+}(aq) + H_2(g)$$
$$Zn^{2+}(aq) + CO_3^{2-}(aq) \rightarrow ZnCO_3(s)$$

22.5   (a) Zinc and magnesium have the following similarities: their cations are 2+ ions of similar size, they are colorless, and they both form hexahydrates. Both elements form soluble chlorides and sulfates, and insoluble carbonates. The anhydrous chlorides are covalently bonded and hygroscopic. However, zinc hydroxide is amphoteric, whereas magnesium hydroxide is basic.

(b) Although both metals form colorless cations, that of zinc has a +2 oxidation state and that of aluminum has a +3 oxidation state. In fact, the only two common features are that both zinc and aluminum are amphoteric metals, reacting with both acids and bases, and they are both strong Lewis acids, their soluble salts forming strongly acidic solutions.

22.7   The charging reactions will be

$$Cd(OH)_2(s) + 2\ e^- \rightarrow Cd(s) + 2\ OH^-(aq)$$
$$2\ Ni(OH)_2(s) + 2\ OH^-(aq) \rightarrow 2\ NiO(OH)(s) + 2\ H_2O(l) + 2\ e^-$$

22.9   Cadmium metal was used as a coating for paper clips primarily because it was a 'sacrificial anode' – meaning that it was oxidized to give white cadmium compounds rather than the iron of the paper clip itself which would rust and stain the paper document. Cadmium was used in preference to zinc probably because cadmium melts at only 421°C, compared with 419°C for zinc, making it easier to dip the paper clip wire into molten cadmium easier than with molten zinc. As cadmium compounds are highly toxic, cadmium plating has been discontinued.

22.11 $Zn(s) + 2 H^+(aq) \rightarrow Zn^{2+}(aq) + H_2(g)$

$Zn(OH_2)_6^{2+}(aq) + 4 NH_3(aq) \rightarrow Zn(NH_3)_4^{2+}(aq) + 6 H_2O(l)$

$Zn^{2+}(aq) + 2 OH^-(aq) \rightarrow Zn(OH)_2(s)$

$Zn(OH)_2(s) + 2 OH^-(aq) \rightarrow Zn(OH)_4^{2-}(aq)$

$Zn(OH)_2(s) \rightarrow ZnO(s) + H_2O(l)$

$ZnO(s) + 2 H^+(aq) \rightarrow Zn^{2+}(aq) + H_2O(l)$

$ZnCO_3(s) \rightarrow ZnO(s) + CO_2(g)$

Beyond the Basics

22.13   Mercury(I) undergoes a disproportionation equilibrium:

$Hg_2^{2+}(aq) \rightarrow Hg(l) + Hg^{2+}(aq)$

This equilibrium is driven to the right by the formation of highly insoluble (high lattice energy) compounds such as mercury(II) selenide:

$Hg^{2+}(aq) + Se^{2-}(aq) \rightarrow HgSe(s)$

22.15   For metals to mix, they must have atoms of similar sizes and adopt the same crystal packing arrangement (see Chapter 4). The metals are very different in size, and data tables show that they have different packing arrangements (lead is cubic close-packed while zinc is hexagonal close-packed).

22.17   Sulfur. Mercury(II) is a soft acid. Sulfur is a soft base whereas oxygen is a hard base.

22.19   (a) $Zn(NH_2)_2(NH_3) + 2 NH_4^+(NH_3) \rightarrow Zn(NH_3)_4^{2+}(NH_3)$

(b) $Zn(NH_2)_2(NH_3) + 2 NH_2^-(NH_3) \rightarrow Zn(NH_2)_4^{2-}(NH_3)$

22.21   Zinc oxide. The (+2)(−2) ionic attractions will be greater than those between (+2) and (−1) ions. In other words, the lattice energy of zinc oxide will be much greater than that of zinc chloride. [In fact, zinc oxide has a melting point of 1975°C while that of zinc chloride is 732°C].

22.23   Hydrogen sulfide is in a two-step equilibrium with the sulfide ion.

$H_2S(aq) + H_2O(l) \rightarrow H_3O^+(aq) + HS^-(aq)$

$HS^-(aq) + H_2O(l) \rightarrow H_3O^+(aq) + S^{2-}(aq)$

In neutral conditions, $[S^{2-}]$ must be greater than the value necessary for the K_{sp} for zinc sulfide to be exceeded. However, when acidified, the increased hydronium-ion concentration will "drive" the equilibria to the left; presumably sufficiently to decrease $[S^{2-}]$ below the necessary value for zinc sulfide precipitation.

Chapter 23

ORGANOMETALLIC CHEMISTRY

Exercises

23.1   (a)   organometallic

        (b)   not organometallic as the bond B-O not B-C

        (c)   organometallic

        (d)   not organometallic as nitrogen is not metallic

        (e)   not organometallic as there is no Na-C bond

        (f)   organometallic

        (g)   organometallic

23.3   (a) $Bi(CH_3)_5$

        (b) $Si(C_6H_5)_4$ tetraphenyl silane

        (c) $KB(C_6H_5)_4$ postassium teraphenylborane

        (d) $Li_4(CH_3)_4$

        (e) $(C_2H_5)MgCl$

23.5 C_2H_5MgBr will be tetrahedral with two molecules of solvent coordinated to the magnesium. In contrast, the bulky organo group in $2,4,6\text{-}(CH3)_3C_6H_2MgBr$ leads to a coordination number of two.

23.7   A transmetallation reaction involves the breaking of the metal-carbon bond and the forming of a metal-carbon bond to a different metal. Mercury compounds are commonly used in transmetallation to form organometallic compounds of other metals.

      $Hg(CH_3)_2 + 2\,Na \rightarrow 2\,NaCH_3 + Hg$

23.9   (a) $CH_3Br + 2\,Li \rightarrow LiCH_3 + LiBr$

        (b) $MgCl_2 + 2\,LiC_2H_5 \rightarrow 2\,LiCl + Mg(C_2H_5)_2$

        (c) $Mg + (C_2H_5)_2Hg \rightarrow Mg(C_2H_5)_2 + Hg$

        (d) $C_2H_5Li + C_6H_6 \rightarrow Li(C_6H_5) + C_2H_6$

        (e) $Mg + C_2H_5HgCl \rightarrow C_2H_5MgCl + Hg$

(f) $B_2H_6 + CH_3CH=CH_2 \rightarrow B(CH_2CH_2CH_3)_3$

(g) $SnCl_4 + 4\ C_2H_5MgCl \rightarrow Sn(C_2H_5)_4 + 4\ MgCl_2$

23.11 (a)   hexacarbonylchromium(0)

(b)   ferrocene or bis(pentahaptocyclopentadienyl)iron(II)

(c)   hexahaptobenzenetricarbonylchromium(0)

(d)   pentahaptocyclopentadienyltricarbonyltungsten(I)

(e)   bromopentacarbonylmanganese(I)

23.13 $Cr(CO)_6$

Cr(0) electrons ($4d^6$)		= 6
CO electrons = 6 x 2		= 12
	Total	= 18

$Fe(CO)_5$

Fe(0) electrons ($4d^8$)		= 8
CO electrons = 5 x 2		= 10
	Total	= 18

$Ni(CO)_4$

Ni(0) electrons ($4d^{10}$)		= 10
CO electrons = 4 x 2		= 8
	Total	= 18

23.15 $V(CO)_6$ is a seventeen electron complex. Therefore, it readily gains another electron to give eighteen.

23.17 (a)

Mn(0) electrons ($4d^7$)		= 7
CO electrons = 5 x 2		= 10
	Total	= 17 therefore 1 Mn–Mn bond

(b)   Mn(I) electrons ($4d^6$)   = 6

CO electrons = 2 x 2   = 4
η^5-C$_5$H$_5$ electrons   = 6
                           total   = 16   therefore 2 Mn–Mn bonds

(c)   Fe(0) electrons 4d^8 = 8
      CO electrons = 2 x 2   = 4
      η^4-C$_4$H$_4$ electrons   = 4
      μ -CO electrons = 2 ÷2   = 1
                           total   = 17   therefore 1 Fe–Fe bond

(d)   Mn(I) elecrtrons (4d^6)   = 6
      CO electrons   = 4 x 2   = 8
      μ-Br electrons = 2 x 2   = 4
                           total   = 18   therefore no Mn-Mn bonds

23.19 (a)   [Cr(CO)$_6$] + 3 CH$_3$CN → [Cr(CO)$_3$(CH$_3$CN)$_3$] + 3 CO

(b)   [Mn$_2$(CO)$_{10}$] + H$_2$ → 2 [HMn(CO)$_5$]

(c)   [Mo(CO)$_6$] + (CH$_3$)$_2$PCH$_2$CH$_2$P(Ph)CH$_2$CH$_2$P(CH$_3$)$_2$ →
[Mo(CO)$_3$((CH$_3$)$_2$PCH$_2$CH$_2$P(Ph)CH$_2$CH$_2$P(CH$_3$)$_2$)] + 3 CO

(d) $[Fe(CO)_5]$ + 1,3-cyclohexadiene → 2 CO $(CO)_3Fe-$
+

(e)

$[NaMn(CO)_5]$ + $CH_2=CHCH_2Cl$ ⟶ NaCl + $[(CO)_5MnCH_2CH=CH_2]$

⟶ $(CO)_5Mn-$ + CO

(f)

$[Cr(CO)_6]$ + C_6H_6 ⟶ $(CO)_3Cr-$ + 3 CO

(g)

$[PtCl_2(PMe_3)_2]$ + $LiCH_2CH_2CH_2CH_2Li$ ⟶   2 LiCl + $(PMe_3)_2Pt$

(h) $[Ni(CO)_4]$ + PF_3 → $[Ni(CO)_3PF_3]$ + CO

(i) $[Mn_2(CO)_{10}]$ + Br_2 → 2 $[Mn(CO)_5Br]$

(j) $[HMn(CO)_5]$ + CO_2 → $[(CO)_5MnCOOH]$

23.21   (a)   Iridium (III)

(b)   Charge on H_3^+ would be +1.

H_3^+ would have 2 electrons over the H-H-H bonds. These would be 2 electron 3 centre bonds, as in diborane.

Beyond the Basics
23.23

$(\eta^5-C_5H_5)_2Ni$ + $Ni(CO)_4$ ⟶   2

23.25

$Na(\eta^5-C_5H_5)W(CO)_3 + CH_2=CHCH_2Cl \longrightarrow NaCl + (CO)_3W$

$CH_2CH=CH_2$

A

hυ   HCl/KPF$_6$

$NaCl + (CO)_2W$

B

$(CO)_3W$

$CH_3CH \dot{=} CH_2$

C

A = tricarbonyl(η^5-cyclopentadienyl)(η^1-propenyl)tungsten(II)
B = dicarbonyl(η^5-cyclopentadienyl)(η^3-propenyl)tungsten(II)
C = tricarbonyl(η^5-cyclopentadienyl)(η^2-propenyl)tungsten(II)
hexafluorophosphate
Evolved gas = propene

23.27   The reaction of alkylated titanium(IV) with carbon disulfide will give
Ti(S$_2$CEt$_2$)$_4$.

23.29

$[Mn_2(CO)_{10}] + Cl_2 \longrightarrow 2\ Mn(CO)_5Cl \xrightarrow{NaC_5H_5} (CO)_3Mn \bigcirc + NaCl$

A   B

$(CO)_3ClMn \bigcirc + 2\ CO$

C

Chapter 24

THE RARE EARTH AND ACTINOID ELEMENTS

Exercises

24.1 (a) $2\ Eu(s) + 6\ H_2O(l) \rightarrow 2\ Eu(OH)_3(s) + 3\ H_2(g)$

(b) $UO_3(s) + H_2SO_4(aq) \rightarrow (UO_2)SO_4(aq) + H_2O(l)$

24.3 If the solubilities of the common salts of the europium 2+ ion are parallel to those of the strontium ion, we would expect the nitrate and chloride to be soluble and the sulfate and carbonate to be insoluble.

24.5 As a 4+ hydrated ion, it is likely to be highly acidic.

$[Ce(OH_2)_6]^{4+}(aq) + H_2O(l) \rightarrow [Ce(OH_2)_5(OH)]^{3+}(aq) + H_3O^+(aq)$

24.7 The shorter half-lives of actinium and protactinium can be accounted for by the fact that they have odd numbers of protons (see Chapter 2).

24.9 The oxidation states of the early actinoids match with those of the transition metals above them. For example, thorium has a common oxidation number of +4 like titanium, zirconium, and hafnium (compare Figure 21.5 with Table 19.2). Uranium has an interesting parallel with chromium: it forms the yellow $U_2O_7^{2-}$ ion like the orange $Cr_2O_7^{2-}$ ion.

Beyond the Basics

24.11 The U^{4+} ion is the most thermodynamically stable, while uranium metal is a very strong reducing agent. The UO_2^{2+} ion in which uranium has an oxidation state of +6 is not significantly oxidizing, as might be expected from the high positive state. The UO_2^+ ion is prone to disproportionation. The U^{3+} is reasonably stable but it can be oxidized to the U^{4+} ion.

24.13 $Mt = [Rn]7s^2 5f^{14} 6d^7$.

24.15 They both adopt the same crystal packing arrangement and they have similar metallic radii (Ti = 145 pm, U = 139 pm) [see criteria for alloy formation in Chapter 4, Section 4.5].

24.17   The reaction will be:

$$^{209}_{83}\text{Bi} + \,^{64}_{28}\text{Ni} \rightarrow \,^{272}_{111}\text{Rg} + \,^{1}_{0}\text{n}$$

The isotope must be Rg-272.